Empowerment and Older People

A Practical Approach

by

Joy Bounds and Helen Hepburn

ISBN 0 948680 46 6

Acknowledgements

Special thanks to Marilyn Harvey and Liz Ward, who gave us some particular help with this book, and to all our friends for their support.

Thanks also to all our colleagues working with older people in the context of community care with whom we have debated the issues and who have thus unwittingly contributed to this book.

The Authors

Helen Hepburn is a trainer in Community Care for a Local Authority and is also involved in counselling. She works for the Grandparants' Federation and has recently written the Advocacy Unit for a National Extension College distance learning pack.

Joy Bounds is a manager in a Social Services Department and many of her responsibilities relate to work with older people and their services. She is a freelance writer and has had several articles published in national magazines on related topics.

Both Helen and Joy have a strong committment to equal opportunities.

Contents Guide

Introduction

Why Empowerment?

Speaking of the new National Health Service and Community Care Act in 1990, the Department of Health said:

> "the rationale for this re-organisation is the empowerment of users and carers. Instead of users and carers being subordinate to the wishes of service-providers, the roles will be progressively adjusted. In this way, users and carers will be enabled to exercise the same power as consumers of other services. This redressing of the balance of power is the best guarantee of a continuing improvement in the quality of the service."[1]

Any discussion of empowerment takes as its starting point an imbalance of power and the need for change. To feel powerless and vulnerable is, to a greater or lesser extent, a part of human experience, whether it be in our personal relationships, in the workplace or in our day-to-day contact with organisations.

In this book we focus on a group of people whose everyday powerlessness, of the sort we all may experience, has become compounded by age and the inability to manage daily life because of illness and/or frailty. How such people are enabled to ask for, and receive, the health and social care they need forms the content.

Older people as equal citizens

Throughout the book, we have considered the position of older people as equal citizens. Older people are, after all, what we shall all become if we do not die prematurely and it is a strange fact of our society at this particular point in time that discrimination is so rife. Individual older people may be regarded highly, but as a group they are stereotyped as of little value. If they are from a minority ethnic background, or are severely disabled, or have dementia, the disadvantage can be compounded.

A practical approach to empowerment

We write from a perspective of "What can we do here and now?" We accept that there may be many different ways of organising health and

4

welfare services, perhaps enabling people to purchase their own care by direct payments to them, or through insurance and pension schemes. To have the money in one's hand, however it arrives there, might appear to be the ultimate way of empowering people. For some it will be. Others, however, are not able to organise their own care and ensure its quality; others will not wish to do so.

But the main reason for exploring empowerment within the current situation is to give some ideas to those working in the care sector who are interested in improving their practice by working in partnership with people and who wish to adopt some strategies in their own workplace.

Our basic premise is that if the older person is to feel empowered, this will largely take place at the point where that person meets their worker face-to-face. This does not absolve the whole organisation of the requirement to direct and support that effort through its policies, structures and human resource management. However, empowerment of staff has not been our focus, though better outcomes for individuals will be assisted by that process. Similarly, our focus has not been on involving older people in the general planning of services, though that also remains an immense challenge to organisations.

What do we call people?

We have struggled with terminology. What should we call people who come to us for assistance? In health care the word 'patient' seems to go unchallenged, though it resonates with the power imbalance. Social services departments have by and large abandoned 'client' with its similar overtones and move uneasily between 'consumer', 'customer', 'user' and 'service-user', and probably more besides. The change in terms reflects a desire to create a different relationship between the individual and the organisation, to convey the idea that people have similar rights to customers, if not the same choices. Others feel that 'customer' implies a commercial relationship we do not have, and adopt the more passive term 'service-user' for want of anything better. We have done the same but tried to avoid such words wherever possible.

Older people, especially those in receipt of services, also have to suffer the indignity of being classed as 'the elderly'. Again this is a term we have tried to avoid, though it does appear in the literature.

5

Unavoidable, however, in discussion of social care and older people is the jargon which has grown up around the processes of deciding what services should be provided – 'eligibility criteria', 'care management', 'care package', to name but a few. Hopefully we have explained the meaning of this jargon as we go along and have tried not to let it mask what is actually happening.

Outline of the book

In the first part, we give a brief history of welfare services in relation to older people. It is chastening to note how short this history is, how recently it was that individual assessment was thought to be necessary, or any regard paid to service preferences. We then look at some theoretical models for imbalances in power between organisations and people and how these can start to be equalised especially in care agencies.

In subsequent chapters, we try to tease out some of the relevant issues as people go through the process of becoming a 'service-user'. We look at some ways of recognising and supporting unpaid carers in their task and also explore some of the specific issues where people have dementia.

In the final section, we take a look at some of the main services – day centres, domiciliary and residential care, and the difficulties of empowering people whilst providing such services.

Finally

Our intention in writing this book is to support staff and their immediate managers who are working directly with older people and their carers. Although we come from a social services background, we write from a perspective of the need for all agencies to co-ordinate their work. The context is difficult. The sheer numbers of people needing services can cause compromise in some of the values we believe in. We operate in a continuous debate about what can be afforded - quality standards hit against this reality every day. That the NHS and Community Care Act has given an opportunity to carve out a space where the needs and rights of older people can be considered, sometimes seems a triumph in itself. We hope that this book will both celebrate this and move the debate forward.

Chapter One

Older People: "The Welfare" and Disempowerment

An Historical Perspective

Introduction

To understand why it has been seen as necessary to incorporate such principles as empowerment, choice and equal opportunities into more recent legislation, it helps to look back at the history of social welfare and discriminatory attitudes. These attitudes have been paternalistic and ageist which, alongside the concepts of the 'deserving and undeserving poor' have meant that many older people had no opportunity to experience dignity and a good quality of life.

Social Welfare – a limited choice

"Historically, the problem of the elderly has been seen as a problem of their destitution." (Parker 1990)

Until 1948, public assistance authorities were responsible for the provision of residential and hospital institutions and for financial allowances for people who were classed as 'destitute'. The workhouse was seen as a deterrent within the Poor Law, signifying poverty amongst certain parts of the population as a personal and moral failure.

The Poor Law was abolished in 1948 and the National Assistance Act, which replaced it, required the provision of accommodation and limited home care by welfare departments which were part of local borough councils, for ill, disabled and older people. However, because of a lack of resources due to the cost of the war, people who had no means of their own nor any family or friends to support them at home continued to be looked after in converted workhouses and in poor law hospital buildings, often with the same staff with the same discriminatory attitudes. Older people's existence was one of minimal provision and a resulting lack of choice and quality of life.

Permissive powers were given in 1948 to make grants to voluntary organisations to provide meals-on-wheels and recreational facilities, for example, luncheon clubs – sometimes with craft-based activities provided. This was haphazard because it depended on pools of people who were willing to deliver the service, on available premises and on transport to get there.

The 1960s and 1970s – improved services for older people?

During this period, there was pressure from academics and politicians to improve the provision of welfare services, which included the creation of integrated social services for children and adults.

In 1962, local authorities were permitted to provide their own meals service but in 1968, under the Health Services and Public Health Act, and in 1970, under the Chronically Sick and Disabled Act, the newly created social services departments were given responsibility for promoting the welfare of older people in their own homes. They were obliged to set up a home help service, but this service was limited and did not meet the needs of those who required assistance with personal care. It mainly provided a cleaning, washing, shopping and pension collection service to older people once or twice a week.

Local authorities added to existing voluntary day services by opening parts of their residential homes to provide day services and, more rarely, by opening custom-built day centres. Health authorities opened day units in hospitals for rehabilitation purposes. None of this day provision was systematically planned and it continued to lead to large disparities in the levels of provision, including a variation in purpose, staffing and times of opening, rather than responding to identified need.

Local health authorities were also able to provide a limited nursing service in people's homes under the National Health Services Act 1977, but priority was often given to mothers and babies.

Despite various legislation, resources did not match the requirements to provide services. The only expansion possible in the community was by shifting resources from residential and long-term hospital care to community care and this proved difficult to achieve.

Since the 1960s

Care in the community has been seen as the most appropriate form of care. For instance, in the consultative document 'Priorities for Health and Personal Social Services in England, 1976':

> "the DHSS reasserted the importance of keeping the elderly in their own homes for as long as possible. To assist this, it was argued, domiciliary services needed to be increased by substantial amounts". (Phillipson 1982)

However, soon afterwards, there were public expenditure cuts by both Labour and Conservative governments, which led to a reduction in many areas of domiciliary and day services.

Residential care was redefined as being part of the community, despite research which showed that most residential care was far from being homely and responsive to individual need. In a study of 124 local authority, voluntary and private homes in the London area:

> "only 18% could be described as providing a home, in the true sense, for their residents and, at the other end of the scale, 15% were categorised as 'institutional' and described as 'rigid', 'unrelaxed' and 'tense'. In very few of the homes was there any form of consultation with the residents about the way life was organised; . . ." (Norman 1980)

Within all of this legislation, there was no requirement to assess people's needs and, therefore, local authorities could simply fail to decide whether someone was in need of services and not provide them. There was no systematic way of knowing what need existed within the community and, therefore, no systematic means of planning to meet those needs. Budgets were attached to existing services, resulting in people being 'slotted in' on a 'take it or leave it' basis and therefore there was little incentive to change.

The 1980s – promotion of 'choice'?

As a result of changes in social security regulations in the early 1980s, older people on low incomes were able to access residential and nursing care without an assessment of need, via direct payments from DHSS. This resulted in a massive increase in expenditure and a burgeoning of private residential and nursing homes to meet the increased demand.

Frail and dependent people were discharged from increasingly expensive hospital care into residential care, nursing home care and community hospitals. Despite continuing efforts to improve the quality of services offered by institutions, most people still wished to remain at home. This was only possible for those with support from their families and friends (predominantly women) and for those with means to pay privately for personal care. The very limited nature of personal care services meant that a few people without means were enabled to remain at home, many of them because of the goodwill of home helps.

1990s and beyond – working towards empowerment?

With the aim of controlling this rapidly rising expenditure, social security funds were transferred to local authorities under the NHS and Community Care Act 1990, with a requirement to separate purchasing powers from providing services. Section 7 (1)(a) required an assessment of needs to be carried out by the purchasing part of the local authority, within the principle of enabling people to remain in their own homes, with people only able to access services if they met criteria defined by the local authorities. By separating budgets from provider services, the Act attempts to promote partnership with dependent people and their carers, enabling them to choose from a much wider range of services from within the statutory, voluntary and private sectors (and to promote competition and value for money). The 1990 Act also requires that the needs of unpaid carers are taken into account. This has been strengthened by the Carers (Recognition and Services) Act 1995, which requires the needs of carers to be assessed if they wish, where the person they care for is entitled to an assessment.

Provision of all kinds is still relatively haphazard, with the private sector having a larger share of the market. The demands on community services by people wishing to remain at home have led to a development of personal home care services, with a rapid increase in unregulated private domiciliary care provision. Some day services are being asked to adapt in ways they were never set up or staffed to do. Specialist services, such as day care for people with dementia, are gradually being developed. However, lack of consistent provision, particularly in rural areas, may mean that people's needs are unable to be met locally. The National Health Service is also coming under financial pressure and managers are anxious to use beds 'efficiently' and provide a medical service alone; therefore stays in hospital are becoming briefer. Health services are defining when they will provide continuing care on the basis of medical need.

Community health services are being stretched as more people are enabled to remain in the community despite increasing levels of frailty. By and large, the care in the community policy is assisting more people to remain at home with what can be very complex packages of care. The financial pressure on local authorities is ironically leading them to impose ceilings on the amounts they will pay for domiciliary care, thereby reducing choice for very dependent people. The very real gains of the NHS and Community Care Act are already being compromised by inadequate resources.

The Effects of Discrimination

Older people's life chances are compounded by discrimination on the grounds of age, class, race, ability, sexual orientation and so on. This often adds up to a lack of regard for the ability of dependent older people to have any power over their own lives.

According to research into the attitudes of social workers in relation to older people:

> "antipathy is often expressed towards working with the elderly. Numerous studies of social work practice appear to confirm a view of the elderly as a low-status group, whose demands for aids and meals-on-wheels can be consigned to the responsibility of unqualified staff and volunteers." (Brearley 1975)

Older people with means have always been able to live in hotels or in private residential and nursing homes, or to pay live-in nurses and housekeepers. Of those who cannot do so, widowed or divorced women are often disadvantaged by their economic dependency on the state or on men, resulting in poverty in old age because they are not able to build up pension rights of their own.

11

The age at which retirement happens has varied according to economic requirements. Classically, some women were encouraged to become economically inactive after the war to make way for the employment needs of men. This in turn affected those women's pension prospects. Some women continued to fill poorly paid, often part-time, caring and cleaning positions in hospitals and care homes, with poor conditions of service, again leading to a lack of money in old age. Demographically, women live longer than men, compounding their economic dependence on reduced state pensions and income support into their 80s and 90s.

The number of black elders is increasing in Britain. These elders are not only affected by class, gender and age inequalities, but also by cultural and language barriers and by racism, at both an institutional and an individual level. Because of a racist assumption about black families 'looking after their own', services have not necessarily been planned in a way which is sensitive to their needs.

The general prejudice against homosexuality extends into older gay men and lesbians, making it even more difficult than other older people to express their sexuality.

Civil rights and consumer movements

The civil rights movements of the 1960s largely ignored the needs of older citizens. Older people have therefore not been enabled to voice their own concerns within these movements. Consequently, only established voluntary agencies were seen as representing the views of older people. More recently, movements such as the Gray Panthers in the USA and trade unions and pensioners groups together in this country have organised protests against the effects of cuts in social welfare and other expenditure on their lives.

In the social welfare field, it was not until the late 1960s that anyone thought to ask consumers how they experienced social work and health intervention.

> "As well as satisfying social work's curiosity, it was recognised that the provision of an effective service requires us to know something about the responses and reactions of those we seek to help." (Sainsbury 1975)

Some people illustrated feelings of disempowerment:

"Many clients felt confused, baffled and even irritated by social workers who were vague or unclear about their intentions." (Howe 1987a)

One woman found her experience with social workers:

"extremely unsatisfactory . . . because they never explained procedures to us so we never knew what the next stage would be or how many hurdles lay in front of us." (Howe 1987b)

The few personal accounts we have of people's experiences in residential and nursing care show us how helpless they can feel about having any control over their own lives, particularly if they were transferred straight from hospital to residential or nursing homes, and their ability to articulate their wishes was easily overridden. People said it was virtually impossible to leave and go back to their own homes if their health improved or if they didn't really need to be there in the first place.

It is generally difficult to find out whether older people have any complaints about services. Surveys which have tried to find out how older people feel tend to find that they are reluctant to criticise services, perhaps because of their dependency on them and a fear of their withdrawal.

In conclusion, the historical background to the provision of services to older people is not a very positive one. It is not surprising to find it echoed today, despite a commitment to good practice and changes in legislation.

Chapter Two

Empowerment – Theory and Reality

'empower' –1. to give or delegate power or authority to; authorise
2. to give ability to, enable or permit

(Collins English Dictionary)

How can the concept of empowerment within the care in the community legislation be effective against the weight of historical, social and economic disadvantage? 'Empowerment' can only make sense within a discussion about the distribution of power and discrimination against certain groups of people. It is only necessary in relation to some potentially disempowering factor – in a world where everyone had equal access to power and resources, people would easily act on their own behalf. They would have no problem in speaking out for themselves, in the fairly certain knowledge that they would be heard and, once heard, that others would respond willingly and freely.

Actually, of course, there are many reasons why any one individual has less access to power and resources than others. Individuals may be disempowered by other individuals or by institutions and structures.

Theories of Empowerment

In trying to define exactly what empowerment means in practice within organisations, it may be helpful to look briefly at different ways of interpreting 'empowerment'. There is no concept of empowerment outside the intention that things will change.

The Exchange Model

This challenges the 'medical model' of interaction where the expert questions the 'patient', diagnoses what is wrong with them and prescribes a solution. The Exchange Model talks about interaction, where the person is an expert on self and workers use their expertise and knowledge to empower or enable the person to come to his or her own solutions. Within this model, the worker respects people's own individual strengths and existing social networks and offers information on every aspect of the options available. Discrimination will be minimised because the person will be wholly involved in finding their own solutions.

Psychological/Structural Model

Individuals cannot be empowered by others, but can be enabled to empower themselves – (psychological). They can be disempowered by institutions (structural). In the relationship between organisations and those who are affected by them, staff must work to enable individuals to empower themselves and also take opportunities to remove structural barriers to empowerment. How does this work out in practice?

Individual: People will differ in their expectations and ability to empower themselves, according to their own individual experiences. They will have had greater or lesser power according to a number of psychological, social and economic factors and this may change over the course of their lives. If they have been discriminated against because of gender, race, culture, poverty or sexuality, they may already feel stigmatised and experience feelings of worthlessness and helplessness. The effects of dependency may lead to individual feelings of low self-esteem, loss of confidence and passivity, and may lead the older person to have low expectations of how much they can influence what happens to them. What happened to people in the past will influence their ability to empower themselves as they become dependent on others.

Empowerment is not about workers abandoning their responsibilities to others. It is a dynamic process of working alongside those who are in the position of having to ask. It requires trust, openness and honesty. Statutory workers will have to listen actively, offer time to think, analyse options and negotiate solutions to meet needs in partnership with people. They will have to set aside their own cultural values and listen to what is 'normal' in that person's life and be flexible in response to people's right to take risks. The probability of a successful outcome will have to be evaluated together as part of this process.

15

Structural: Structural disempowerment is about the way in which organisations act without any regard for the individual, e.g. through bureaucratic processes which do not make sense to the service-user and which do not seem to make meeting their needs a priority.

M Taylor et al (1992) use a 'ladder of participation' to tease out what 'empowerment' might mean within public services.

High   Users have the authority to take decisions;
        Users have authority to take some decisions;
        Users have an opportunity to influence decisions;
        User views are sought before making decisions;
        Decisions are publicised and explained before
        implementation
Low   Information is given about decisions made.

(Taylor et al 1992)

This model is relevant to the way in which organisations make it possible for staff to empower people. For example, some organisations put a lot of effort into consulting with users and, if taken seriously, this would place them higher up the ladder. Users would have to have the money and be able to buy their own services to be at the top. However users will not feel empowered at all if they are simply told about what decisions have already been made, for example, if services are withdrawn without consultation.

The Market Model – 'exit' and "voice'

This model presupposes that people can empower themselves by 'exiting' from a service in order to go to a better one, or have a 'voice' in changing the service they are using. Taylor et al (1992) point out that the implications of applying competition and choice to health and social services denies the complexities of 'choosing' such personal services. Although the NHS and Community Care Act attempts to bring the concept of market forces into public sector services and it advocates the principles of empowerment, partnership and choice, are people who are dependent on public services really able to exercise these two alternatives of 'exit' or 'voice'?

With regard to the concept of 'exit', people may be able to leave a service for whatever reason, but in doing so could leave themselves vulnerable because they cannot access another without departmental agreement.

In relation to 'voice', someone in a residential home, for example, may be satisfied with one aspect of the home and not others. How will she make this known? When will someone stop long enough in their busy schedules to listen? Is she seen as a person worthy of an opinion about her care, especially if she has dementia? She may have built up relationships of trust with staff or live near her relatives and not want to 'exit' from the home, but she may still want to make changes for herself. Those whose thinking powers are impaired will not be able to participate very easily, if at all, in either process.

The consumer concepts of 'exit' and 'voice' are useful but ultimately limited for dependent older people within a welfare setting. Despite efforts to minimise the disempowering effects of organisations, they cannot by their very nature truly share power.

Advocacy

In order to redress the balance of power, pressure groups talk about the necessity of various forms of advocacy.

Self-advocacy, a term only applied to those who are dependent (it is called 'speaking up for yourself' for those who are not) is the ideal, but this relies on staff to listen and respond to people's wishes for change. Group advocacy in the form of residents and unpaid carers forums can be effective but are not representative of everyone's views. Citizen advocacy at least means that an older person could have access to an independent voice, advocating on their behalf. Citizen advocacy networks are not very well developed for older people – evidence of ageist attitudes towards this group of people.

Community development, such as in developing support for carers, or self-help groups for those with similar experiences, can shift the power imbalance towards the community.

The Imbalance of Power

With some understanding of the different ways of looking at empowerment, we are in a better position to explore the power imbalance between vulnerable older people and the agency to whom they come for assistance. Such agencies might be health authorities or trusts, social services departments, the voluntary or private sector, housing departments and so on. Greater understanding of this unequal equation will assist us to see why empowerment is such a challenge.

Who decides?

On a day-to-day basis, the professional agencies have immense power over individuals. The social services department will decide, for example, how urgently it views a person's situation, what sort of professional will be asked to make an assessment, and what indeed it will define as a need which it is prepared to meet from its resources. This can appear extremely arbitrary. Some areas, for example, will not provide resources for cleaning a person's home if they can no longer do it themselves; other areas will.

Someone dying of cancer may have a better chance of the health authority providing an overnight nurse than someone who is dying of another condition. Some people with dementia will be excluded from sheltered housing schemes if their behaviour becomes 'difficult to manage'– other schemes appear to have the resources to cope.

The NHS and Community Care Act was perhaps intended to reduce what appears to many to be arbitrary power. It was hoped that the requirement to act on assessed need would ensure a consistency of decision-making in which people could have confidence. In fact, the shortage of resources to fulfil the aims of the legislation means that targeting, rationing and variable budget-led decisions keep the power firmly in the hands of the various authorities.

Scarce resources

There are also other kinds of shortages which inhibit the equalisation of power between the agencies and individuals. A truly empowering assessment, for example, as explored in a later chapter, requires time. The potential service-user normally has a lot of time, especially if their physical safety is assured whilst the process runs on. It is the assessors and their managers who have little time to understand the whole picture and assist the person towards a good outcome.

Pressure on resources within hospital results in an inadequate number of beds. Recovery time may be very short and the consultant may declare the person fit for discharge when they feel anything but ready themselves. This may result in feelings of extreme vulnerability when they go home. Alternatively, fear may lead to a residential care admission when a little more inpatient care could have resulted in a safe discharge home.

Community nursing staffing has not been increased to cope with increasing numbers in the community who need support, and their criteria for what is seen as a nursing task has been tightened. Even voluntary organisations, who increasingly provide services to those no longer regarded as eligible for statutory services, find that stand-still grants lead to prioritisation and ever more complex criteria. The pressure on the private sector to be competitive through local authority contracting processes means that staffing and resources are not always as adequate as owners might like.

Attitudes and the protection of staff

Everyone with a need for community care services has a right to be heard, for staff to be attentive and engaged in the issues presented to them by the individual. Earlier in this chapter, the 'Exchange Model' was explored as a way of achieving this. However, the attitudes of staff will in many ways decide the success of such interactions. A patronising or discriminatory approach will ensure its failure. Similarly, if staff are overworked, they will protect both their time and their emotions in the face of the distress of the people they are there to assist. The outcome will be that staff set the pace and the tone of the interaction, which may not meet the needs of the person.

Conclusion

In this chapter we have explored the concept of 'empowerment' and how disempowerment is part of the relationship between organisations and individuals. Service-user empowerment will need structures, knowledge, resources, commitment and training from power-holders. It will require investment in advocacy networks, and confidence-building for service-users. One could say that the only way to be empowered is for people, or for advocates on their behalf, to have the right to control their own services so that they are not at risk of second-class citizenship.

We are far from such solutions. Many of the issues raised in this chapter are outside the scope of this book – their resolution would need a much greater input of resources and a new concept of 'welfare' which is currently far away. Nevertheless, there is still a great deal that can be done to empower people within current structures and this informs the debate in the following chapters.

Chapter Three

Becoming a User of Services?

What makes it difficult to approach services?

Most people are used to making decisions for themselves, being able to move around freely and conduct their personal lives in their own particular ways. People who are used to this relative independence will struggle on for as long as they can even if daily tasks are becoming a little more difficult, either on their own or with the help of relatives and friends. There may be a reluctance to ask for help from statutory services because it means admitting to not being able to cope. Even visiting general practitioners is done reluctantly for fear of 'bothering' them and for fear of confirmation that there may be something wrong enough to lead to a loss of independence.

To approach local authorities is even more difficult, not least because of a lack of information about how to do so. If people have also had to struggle for months to get out of bed, walk to the shops and so on, then they may well feel that either it will not be bad enough for them to get any help or they fear they will lose all of their ability to control their own lives once they have made that approach for a service.

Easier Access

One clear route

The NHS and Community Care Act requires local authorities and health departments to give good information to the public about access to services. People often approach general practitioners, hospital staff and agencies such as housing departments, citizen advice bureaux and Age Concern about their needs, including their social needs. The Act requires that access to social services should be through one clear well-publicised route, and all agencies need to know what this is.

Information

The Act also requires information about eligibility criteria, assessment processes and services to be given to the public in forms which are easily accessible by all members of the public.

This is an area in which, in order for the public to empower themselves, they, their carers, voluntary agencies, GPs, health visitors, nurses and consultants must know:

- where their nearest office is and how to access it;
- their local authority's definitions of which people have a right to services (eligibility criteria);
- that people have a right to negotiate how their needs can be met through an assessment process;
- what services may be available, and the possible financial implications;
- any standards which have been set for responding to enquiries.

Information is an essential element of enabling people to empower themselves. People need time to consider all their alternatives and need the information in a form that they can understand so that they can take it away with them and discuss it with friends, family and others. This at least means that they are more in control of whether they wish to become service-users.

Becoming a Service-User?

The way in which people become service-users is different for each individual. However, there are common themes.

A crisis

Older people are often precipitated into approaching health and social services departments at times of crisis in their lives, with related feelings of powerlessness, grief and a realistic fear of loss of independence and control over their own lives.

If the person is already becoming dependent on a relative or friend for some of their physical and emotional needs, the crisis may come when that carer is no longer able to support the older person. This is particularly distressing for the dependent person, because it forces them to go to others for help, possibly against their will. Again, it may be that a relative, who may or may not live some way away, is concerned about their increasing frailty and being 'at risk', and will decide that they need to share their concern with professionals. This could be because of a sudden illness or accident. The older person may otherwise be coping reasonably well and find their desire for things to stay as they are being overridden by the relative, neighbour or friend.

Discrimination

People may be subject to discriminatory attitudes which may affect whether they become service-users or not. Ageism can mean that an older person is falsely seen as helpless and unable to take decisions in their own lives. The older person may feel that they have little power to influence what will happen to them. In addition, gender may affect perceptions of how well people should be able to cope on their own, with perhaps neighbours feeling that men must need domiciliary help more than women. Behaviour exhibited by people with mental health problems or dementia, seen as odd or inconvenient, can also lead to a rejection by the person's community.

People from minority ethnic groups may need particular help to access information about services in the form of outreach work, working with interpreters and with key people in their communities.

People who come to this country may be nervous about asking for services, because they may feel they are not entitled. They may have no contact with people outside their own communities, be unable to speak English, have had bad experiences before or heard of others' bad experiences of public services, or feel that their particular religious or cultural needs will not be met. They may need reassurance as well as good information before they feel able to explore the possibilities of using services.

It is for these reasons that front-line staff and other professionals need to approach any request for service from third party referrers from the point of view of empowerment of the potential service-user above all. This must include the issue of consent. In exceptional circumstances, where someone is at high risk of abuse, neglect or self-harm, lack of consent may have to be overridden temporarily.

Approaching the service

People may be fortunate enough to be well informed about services and processes. This knowledge may have come through their own previous experiences or from knowing others who have successfully negotiated their way through the bureaucracy. They may feel able to ask for help themselves or may ask somebody, e.g. a neighbour or friend, to contact the social services office on their behalf. Legal representatives or citizen advocates from voluntary agencies may also have assisted the person to state their needs. With good information and advice from knowledgeable advisers, people are more likely to feel empowered to make decisions about how their needs may be met. This may include choosing not to become a service-user.

The right to take risks

As well as relatives, friends and others deciding what is good for the older person, ageism in the community can be compounded further by institutional discrimination. The NHS and Community Care Act emphasises empowerment, partnership and choice for people. It has tried to shift professional culture from an 'I know what's best' position to an enabling stance.

Professional workers from health and social services need to be aware that people have the right to be at calculated risk. In extreme cases, their liberty can be removed under the Mental Health Act 1983 or National Assistance Act 1948. In the case of people unable to decide for themselves because of mental impairment such as dementia, there are particular dilemmas attached to the concept of risk which have to be struggled with (see Chapter 7).

Initial Information Gathering

Many local authorities are improving their 'front of house' facilities, so that people are received with courtesy and respect when they approach the local authority for the first time. The improvements are in the form of providing open reception areas accessible to people with wheelchairs, with comfortable seating and with rooms where people can ask for and give information privately, and in the provision of trained reception staff who can respond in person or on the telephone. Given the potential stigma of approaching the local authority, people have to feel that they will be welcome and treated with respect by skilled people. This is absolutely crucial if people are to be assisted to identify whether their needs could be met by the local authority.

Interpersonal skills

The most important quality for front of house staff whether they are a trained receptionist, customer services officer or duty worker, is that they are able to listen actively to what is being said. They need to check that they have understood what is being asked at every stage and give information clearly, or find out information if they do not have it readily available. They also need to know where the limits of their authority are so that people's time is not wasted unnecessarily.

The person making an enquiry may be unable to communicate for a variety of reasons. For example, an interpreter or advocate might need to be with the person.

The kinds of questions staff need to explore are:

• Who needs help and why?

- Can the local authority help? If not, what information does the person need about other services so that their needs can be met?

- What information does the older person or their carer need in order to make decisions about whether to take enquiries further?

- After consideration of all information, does the person wish to have an assessment of needs?

- If it is a third party who is requesting an assessment, has the service-user given consent?

- If the person is unable to give consent, what are the reasons for this?

- Does the older person, their carer or third party referrer say the need is urgent?

Recording the request for an assessment

Once people have agreed that an assessment will help them, they need to know that some personal information will be recorded. The principle of empowerment means that people should have control over their own information. Forms should be filled in by the potential service-user themselves if possible. Therefore, forms need to be easily read and understood. This may mean that forms are in large print, in first languages that are not English, in braille, etc.

If the person is unable or does not want to fill in forms themselves, they should be given appropriate assistance. Any record of information must be shown to people to check for accuracy if they were not filled in by the potential service-user themselves. Permission should be sought to ask for or give information to other professionals.

People will feel more in control of processes if they know why information is needed and why it needs to be shared. For example:

- managers can make decisions about who will be the most appropriate person to assist them;

- social work staff and other professionals need to have access to information already gathered by other agencies, so that a person's story does not have to be told over and over again;

- a decision can be made as to how urgent the person's needs are.

Once people have decided that local authorities might be able to meet their needs, they need to have information about how long it might be before they are contacted by an assessor and what that assessment process will be. The Act requires that they are informed of the right to complain at any time during the process and how to do so. They also have a right to see any record made about them.

Conclusion

With limited resources and with empowerment of people in mind, everyone involved needs to be quite clear when it is not appropriate to refer people, thereby unnecessarily raising their expectations, or going against their willingness to become involved in inevitably bureaucratic interventions. Where people are referred or refer themselves, staff need to work from a basis of the person being in control of information and processes as much as possible.

Chapter Four

Enabling Older People to Define their Needs

The NHS and Community Care Act lays emphasis on assessment, a concept which over recent years has come to have great significance in all professions. Assessment is the first part of a process which results in the provision of services and is the understanding and definition of need. In the White Paper 'Caring for People', which preceded the Act, Griffiths (1989) described it as "the cornerstone of good quality care".

However, because the process is necessary when people are vulnerable and exposing their need, it is crucial for it to be done in a way which empowers people. In later chapters, the particular issues relating to the assessment of people in hospital and those with dementia will be explored: also issues as they affect unpaid carers. What follows here is a view of some of the difficulties generally inherent in trying to assess need – not just deciding which services the person can be slotted into – and ways of overcoming them.

What Do People Want from Assessment?

– to understand what is happening

In the previous section we considered how important it is for the person to understand what processes will occur once they have decided to become a service-user and when their need has been accepted. Clear information is equally important at this stage:

- How many visits might the assessor make?
- What might they need to know?
- What form will be filled in?
- Will there be financial implications?
- Whose decision will the outcome be?

– to be understood and enabled to explain

People will want the assessor to be sensitive to the fact that, for the reasons stated before, they may not be comfortable with 'becoming a service-user'. Their need may be great, but hesitancy and uncertainty need to be sensitively handled. Following from this, the person needs to explain their own story, situation and difficulties. Assumptions should not be drawn too quickly. The assessor needs to show that they will respect this and allow the person to go at their own pace, taking responsibility jointly for the outcome.

– to reflect on what is happening

Ageism is such in our society that it is very difficult for older people to reflect on what is happening, except in their own minds, because others do not value them doing this. Sometimes older people themselves are scared to do so; facing the loss of their loved ones, and of their own ability is very painful, especially if the conclusion might have to be to leave one's own home and go into residential or nursing care. Assessors need to be brave enough to help older people reflect on these things and not collude with feelings of being old and disposable.

– not to have to answer irrelevant questions

Sometimes older people and their carers feel angry that any assessment is required at all. They are very clear about what they want – for example, a stair-rail to enable a person with increasing debility through arthritis to continue to sleep upstairs; or someone to help a partner to bed so the carer can go out for the evening a couple of times a week. They can feel devalued by an approach which does not respect the self-assessment they have already done.

Other situations are far more complex and everyone acknowledges that time and effort need to be taken to understand the full picture and explore all the issues.

The NHS and Community Care Act obliges assessors to work to the principle of minimal intervention in terms of assessment. This is not always straightforward – situations can be much more complex than they first seem, especially if there is conflict between family members or the rights of different people impinge on each other. Conversely, endless visits and discussions will be insulting to those who are in control of their situation and are clear about their needs.

– for the family and community network to be explored and supported

It is very easy for assessors unwittingly to cut out small but significant sources of help. The neighbour whose 'only' contribution has been to pop in every Friday with fish and chips for lunch, but sometimes doesn't if other family events occur, might seem easier to replace with a very reliable meals service. In doing so, an important social contact may have been broken, thus increasing the isolation of the service-user within their own community. Carers, family and neighbours may often seem to be saying they are overburdened by the help they are giving, but this does not mean they want to be re-placed – which is a sad loss indeed to the service-user – but supported.

– define what the needs are and re-affirm strengths

Areas of difficulty will have to be discussed and, ultimately, this is where the focus will lie. However, strengths and abilities must be explored and maintained as of equal importance. 'Needs help washing' is far more disempowering than 'Can wash herself if a bowl of water and flannel are placed on her lap'. Not only is ability acknowledged and maintained, but unnecessary feelings of helplessness avoided.

– for gaps to be identified and the person, in discussion with the assessor, to begin to come up with solutions

When options are laid out and full information given, people will begin to find their own solutions, given time to explore what each option might mean for them. This cannot be a mechanical process based on some checklist of need – people need to consider what fits for them. For example, two people with similar physical and mental frailty will not necessarily choose the same option. One may prefer the communal and safety aspects of residential care; the other may prefer the independence, albeit at some risk, of remaining at home. Motivation and 'what fits' the individual and their lifestyle as well as their needs requires time and sometimes patience to establish.

– expertise, but also partnership

The person needs to have confidence in the expertise of the assessor. This expertise will be multifaceted, comprising skills, knowledge and problem-solving ability. It will include the attitude of working in partnership with the person. All of this will be brought to bear on both the process and the outcome of the assessment.

Why is Assessment Difficult?

We continue to try and unravel the strands of assessment as if it were a tangled skein of wool, considering different empowerment models as outlined in Chapter Two. Why should this be? The older person's requirements from assessment are far-ranging, as described, but not beyond the scope of a trained, skilled and sensitive professional. After all, the model we have proposed focuses on the basic human right to respect and choice, on anti-discriminatory practice and interpersonal skills, rather than on any great academic or clinical knowledge.

If assessment were simply a one-to-one transaction between the person and the assessor, it would not be so difficult to attain these requirements. However, assessment is part of, or the start of, an extremely bureaucratic process. To be meaningful, assessment does not stand alone as a pure form. It is not possible to carry out assessment without taking the wider context into account and it is at this point that empowerment in the assessment process becomes more challenging.

Assessment within the Bureaucratic Process

Let us consider assessment from the assessor's point of view. Any single request for assessment, such an important step for the individual, is one of many for a team of assessors. The demand for assessment and other care management tasks is so remorseless that requests have to be prioritised in ways which might shock the new client:

- how high is the risk?
- how near is breakdown point?
- can the person manage another day, another week?

Once the person's perceived needs have a high enough priority for an assessor to visit, it is just one of many calls on a worker's time, to be fitted somehow into a day already packed with activity. It is a constant challenge indeed to the assessor to approach each person afresh, to be sensitive to their newness within the system (or some fresh deterioration warranting a re-assessment), and begin to delicately lay the foundations of an effective relationship.

Secondly, the outcome of the interaction between the individual and the assessor has to be written down. Basic information has to be recorded, the needs defined in writing, ways of meeting those needs analysed on paper, aims, objectives and time-scales drawn up. Any resulting request for funding will have to be presented to a manager – sometimes several managers or panels.

The competition for resources and funding is such that no individual assessment can be considered purely on its merits, however hard assessors try to keep the assessment of need separate from care planning. Comparisons will be drawn with individuals in 'similar' situations; one person's needs may be judged as less pressing than another's. All assessors work in these restricted circumstances and know that a resource gained for one person may mean none for another.

Empowerment – what is it?

The final part of this chapter focuses on some ways assessors can build on their interpersonal and professional skills to work with people in a way which empowers them, yet does not ignore, and tries to satisfy, the demands of the bureaucratic organisation.

Forms

– encourage people to fill in their own forms

The precious contact time between the older person and the assessor does not have to be dominated by form-filling. It can feel bureaucratic and disempowering to individuals if the assessor is sitting there with a form on his or her lap, basically conducting a question and answer session. In addition, the basic requirements of assessment – to get to know the person and understand their situation – will not be met by this process.

Time constraints, plus the immediate need for services to begin in many situations, mean that sometimes forms have to be completed within even the first interview. However, if people can be asked to complete or start the form prior to the assessor's visit, or afterwards if appropriate, then the process takes a rightfully less dominant place and, besides, is far more within the control of the service-user.

– ensure the form follows the natural flow

Not everyone is physically or mentally able to fill in their own form, or may not wish to do so, and there will be times when it is necessary or preferable for the assessor to complete it on the spot. It is helpful if forms are constructed in a way that follows the natural flow of assessment questions, including strengths and networks as well as areas of difficulty, leading to a definition of need and shortfall. Assessors do not need to slavishly follow the format, but can creatively find ways to complete them which fits with their own approach. Needless to say, not all sections should be completed if not relevant to the principle of 'minimum intervention'.

– the service-user's requirement to sign

Most organisations will require the person to sign the assessment forms when complete and this idea seems very empowering. The service-user knows exactly what has been written and their signature symbolises their agreement. However, if no time is given to consider the information required and written on the form, what it means and adds up to, it will just have been another meaningless demand. Moreover, it was not so long ago when people's 'consent' to going into the workhouse or a home was sealed by 'getting their signature' on some papers. In the light of this, it is understandable why people need to be absolutely clear about what they are signing and we need to show sensitivity towards hesitation. Obviously, people need a copy of their forms if they are to feel control within the process.

Co-ordinating everyone's input into assessment

When Griffiths in his White Paper, 'Caring for People', suggested a 'lead assessor' (a role finally given to social services departments, though other individuals from, for example, health and housing departments, can be designated lead assessors on behalf of social services), he did so out of concern that many people can be involved in assessments – if there is no co-ordination, a lot of effort is wasted, duplication occurs, and the person ends up telling their story many times. A good understanding of this by the social worker will save work for herself and tedium and confusion for the older person.

Often people have had contact with several professionals before referral to the social services department – they may have had a district nurse attend, perhaps a spell in hospital, be well known to their GP, have a scheme manager if in sheltered housing, etc. Some of these people may have been approached already through the information-gathering stage, but at the beginning of the assessment the social worker should seek further contact. Better still, they may be able to begin a jointly agreed form.

This empowers the person in the following ways:

– h/she does not have to keep explaining the intentions of these other professionals, who presumably have formed their own action plans which the assessor needs to understand;

– the person gets the feeling of a co-ordinated team communicating well, trusting each other's expertise and working together for a good outcome – true multi-disciplinary assessment is achieved;

– information which lies in several places (the separate notes of every person and agency having input) is collated. It all adds to the totality of the picture the assessor is building up, which assists the reflective discussions being had with the person. This will increase confidence in the assessor and the assessment process.

Anti-oppressive practice

The very term anti-oppressive implies a consciousness of the power imbalance we have touched on throughout this book between the professional worker – whether they belong to health, housing or social services, the private sector or a voluntary body – and the older person who is in a very vulnerable position because we become involved often at a point of breakdown or loss.

The process of equalising the power will be aided by ensuring the ability of the person to participate fully in the assessment. After all, there can be very serious outcomes from these seemingly simple discussions in terms of changes to lifestyle, financial commitment, even relinquishing one's home.

– Is some special equipment needed to compensate for hearing loss?

– Is an interpreter needed if English is not the first language; where would an interpreter best be found?

– Has the person had the opportunity to have a friend/advocate present (was time given to arrange this, encouragement to do so)?

In addition to this, many of our service-users are doubly disadvantaged in that not only do they have this vulnerability at this time, but they may suffer discrimination. Most organisations in the care sector, whether statutory, private or voluntary, will have equal opportunities statements. However, to have a statement does not necessarily mean that the good intentions will be automatically transferred to practice. Assessors need to examine their own attitudes to ensure that they have understood their own prejudices and their effect on their work. They will empower people by opening up these areas within their assessment discussions, exploring people's experience of discrimination and bringing any significant factors through into the care plan.

Specialist Assessors

Many people, for example occupational therapists, nurses, physio-therapists, will be involved in assessments without having the comprehensive role we have just described. They may be asked to do an assessment in a specialist area, for instance, of someone's nursing needs or hearing ability. Good practice as we have described should also govern their contact with the person as well as the desire to work in a co-operative way to ensure a good outcome which meets the older person's needs.

Conclusion

The older person may often appear to be disempowered by vulnerability, age, poor health and the difficulties of entering into a relationship with welfare agencies. Assessment is sometimes a difficult process and a complex one. Nevertheless, the more the assessor works in partnership with the person, encouraging their control of the process, the more likely it is that a successful plan of action will be reached.

Chapter Five

Empowering People in Hospital

Person to 'Patient'

In a later chapter on empowering people who live in residential care, we will explore in more detail the dangers which arise when staff care for residents as a group rather than as individuals. In hospital, the force of institutionalisation is even stronger in some ways. However much staff try to mitigate the effects of managing people who have to be rapidly prepared for and helped to recover from medical procedures, the power remains firmly with the hospital.

How does this feel? It is hard to feel in control when the focus is all on the bed, which is in fact almost all of one's territory, and much of the day is spent in nightclothes. Food is often not to one's choice or even liking; the environment is kept scrupulously clean and tidy; much loved friends and relatives may only be able to visit at certain times, and they can feel equally powerless as they sit on the low chairs by the extraordinarily high bed.

Such feelings of powerlessness will be even more intense in people who do not speak English as their first language, whose cultural needs may be disregarded and to whom procedures may seem very strange and frightening. When the consultant comes with the team of registrars, students and nurses, they all stand whilst the 'patient' lies, or sits half-propped up in bed. Examinations may be cursory, discussions in a jargon which appears to exclude participation. It all feels strange and embarrassing.

Many of us will undergo such experiences in our lives and if we don't much like it, well, we will put up with a lot for the sake of being well and getting back home as quickly as possible.

The reaction of older people in this situation

Fear is likely to be a more dominant feeling for older people going into hospital. Everyone will feel fear if they have a life-threatening illness, of course, but otherwise will hope for successful treatment and a rapid return home. However, older people may be experiencing such a decline in their coping abilities – hospital admission marking the nadir – that, rightly or wrongly, they fear their lives are going to change in a big way.

Maybe they will be too poorly to return home, even after treatment, and fear they will have to stay in a ward or peripheral hospital far from friends. Maybe they will be too frail or disabled to be able to manage at home again and have to move into a residential or nursing home. Even in this last decade of the twentieth century, such a fate may resonate with memories of the workhouse, especially where hospitals still use the same buildings. Older people may not know how much residential and nursing homes try to individualise care – they see it as loss of independence and a familiar, if increasingly difficult, lifestyle.

In addition, older people will fear that they are not going to be able to exercise choice in what happens to them during and at the end of their hospital stay. They are likely to regard the medical staff as 'expert' and feel that the outcome might be the expert opinion and not their own. Even if the person is normally more able to challenge or ignore medical advice, they may fear being unable to make their wishes known. Old, ill in bed, far from home – not a condition conducive to assertiveness and clear thought.

The responsibility of hospital staff

These factors add up to a situation where the older person, especially if they have no family member or friend to help them, will almost inevitably feel disempowered. It is not easy to be an expert on your own life, on your own needs and in control of your own destiny in such a situation.

Older people need all the help they can get from the staff working with them. It is recognised that what happens to people happens because the large institution is committed to rapid turnover; thus a 'named nurse' is appointed to each patient to help them understand what is happening and to do their own preliminary assessment work with them to ensure that all is in place for them to go home. However, the shift system means they are not available all the time.

It is now part of the training and professional values of nurses and other paramedical staff to regard the person and their carers holistic-ally, that is not as just a body which needs patching up and discharging as soon as possible, but as person with their own hopes, fears and ideas, which they have some responsibility to pay regard to.

To enable the patient to feel more in control of what is happening, nurses and other hospital staff need to practise all of the empower-ment strategies we have discussed at every point in this book. They need to ensure that they give the fullest possible information to their patient, about their treatment, what it will entail, how long it will last, whether it stands alone or is part of a more complex plan and what the possible outcomes might be. They need to take time to get to know the person a little, what their circumstances are, who, if anyone, cares for and about them and to involve any such people in the discussions. Using their inter-personal skills, they need to listen to the person, let them express their concerns and understand their future choices.

By working with people in partnership, medical staff can do much to break down the inequalities in power, can help the patient to maintain motivation and, rather than remain silent in fear, explore options for the future. If the discharge home is, after all, relatively straightforward, the named nurse can ensure a smooth discharge by good liaison with anyone in the community actively involved in providing care.

Referral to Social Services

Sometimes it becomes obvious that the situation has changed so much that the person is going to require further discussion about their future. If the 'named nurse' has done her job well thus far, it will cause no problem for her to discuss how a referral to social services might help. Full information can be given about what the process will be, and informed consent given by the person prior to the referral being made to the social worker. Re-assurance can be given that everyone will wish to work in partnership, maintaining the rights of the person to make their own choices.

The social worker will be delighted to find the way so well prepared. Their customer will seem less like a 'patient', knowledgeable about their situation and already geared up to have control over the assessment and care planning process.

The Social Worker Working in a Hospital Setting

The Social Services Inspectorate (1995), in a report on Community Care in Hospitals, said:

> "tensions were sometimes evident between health and social services around efficiency of bed use and the pace of assessment, care planning and discharge. Hospital social workers were often at the sharp end of this and, in some cases, demoralised by its impact."

People from multi-disciplinary settings come from different perspectives and if teams are to succeed they have to work with these conflicts and learn to trust each other's professional basis. However, this is difficult where the culture of the hospital is strong, with its focus on consultant power.

Social work has its professional roots in the philosophy of understanding each individual and their situation in its uniqueness and in advocating for tailor-made solutions. In this sense, the hospital social worker has a difficult task.

They must be an influential part of the multi-disciplinary team, yet retain their own professional focus. This can cause conflict which may feel uncomfortable, especially as the social workers can seem very small in numbers compared with health workers. In addition, social work is often regarded with a certain amount of suspicion by other disciplines, where outcome is perhaps easier to organise. Once a person is 'ready for discharge' (a phrase which normally only refers to the medical situation), the pressure from hospital administrators and the consultant can be fierce – the bed will be needed for someone else. Not only does the social worker have to work fast, but he or she may often be in the position of fighting for the extra day or two which will allow the person to complete the decision-making process without feeling bullied and out-of control – then perhaps reaching an unsuitable outcome.

An example of this is that the person may come to the conclusion as a result of the assessment that a nursing home would best meet their needs. Precious time is now needed for family members at least to look round a couple of homes in the relevant locality, and preferably for the person themselves to spend a few hours there. After all, this is to be their permanent home in the future. Inevitably, this will take a couple of days – days seen in terms of 'turnover' and even 'bed-blocking' by hospital administrators anxious to meet impossible targets. However, it is vital that such time is allowed.

Managers also have a role in making it possible for assessors to concentrate on their main task, without always having to fight with their colleagues. They need to ensure that discharge protocols are kept to, and issues sorted out at the appropriate management level.

Assessment in Hospital

Social workers, either working permanently within the hospital setting or coming in from the community, often wonder if assessment in hospital is really possible at all. We have mentioned some of the ways in which hospitals depersonalise people, how an older person may feel their life is running beyond their control, the pressures of 'turnover', etc. What chance has the social worker of getting to know the person as they 'habitually' are, of understanding their strengths and vulnerabilities, of fitting into the picture the ways in which the family and neighbourhood network supports the person?

Where possible, if safety can be assured, it might be better for the person to be discharged home and for the assessment to continue there, especially if it is likely that such a major decision as entry into residential care may be called for. This would prevent rushed and inappropriate decisions and people and their carers may be surprised at how much they can still manage, with proper help.

If the assessment must take place in hospital, then the social worker needs to bear in mind all the aspects of the assessment process mentioned in the previous chapter: using the information of other professionals; ensuring the person and their carer's involvement in the whole process, including the completion of forms; ensuring sensitivity to any cultural issues; enabling the person to define their own needs.

To achieve this successfully, the assessor needs to make the situation as normal as possible for the person. A private and comfortable room must be found where the social worker can talk with the older person, can continue uninterrupted, with unpaid carers and family members there if appropriate, and the person feeling as though perhaps for a little while they have managed to step outside the hospital routine and can think about their future.

Good Discharge Practice

If a situation has changed enough to warrant an assessment of any depth, it is likely that discharge will seem scary to the person. If they are going on to a new chapter in their life in residential care, they will need a lot of re-assurance that the Home understands their care needs. An early visit by the social worker will help this transition, acknowledge grief and fear and pick up any immediate problems, especially if there are few family members or carers to assist.

If the person is going home with a package of care of any intensity, the assessor's job is a great deal more complex. Liaison with community nurses, care agencies, meal delivery services, day-care transport, etc. must be meticulous. For the package of care to feel safe to the person leaving hospital in a vulnerable position, every small detail must be in place.

Discharge is the beginning of a new process and it is important that the person is not left to deal with this alone. Re-assurance will be given by an early visit to adjust any aspects of the care package not quite meeting need. The assessor will need to see the person in their home environment and the assessment process can continue with the person and the assessor working alongside each other to create the outcome best suited to the particular needs of that person.

Chapter Six

Sharing the Load with Carers

Within the political debates about the NHS and Community Care Act, unpaid carers are often seen as a solution to the demands of an ageing population, care by the community as against care in the community. As a result of research, after the implementation of the Act, which requires that their needs are taken into account, carers groups found that there was no consistency about meeting carers' needs. Under pressure, the government passed the Carers (Recognition and Services) Bill 1995, which has come on to the statute book in April 1996, giving carers who offer a substantial amount of care to dependent people a right to request a separate assessment of needs if the cared for person is entitled to an assessment.

Carers are sometimes left out of the process of assessing the needs of the dependent person. They may not see themselves as 'carers' in the formal sense of the word and therefore may not recognise that they have a right to have their own needs met. Their care may be 'invisible' and their own needs may be ignored. On the other hand, where the cared for person is unable to speak up for themselves, the needs of carers may come to override the needs of the dependent person, thereby disempowering them.

Who are the carers?

It is important to understand who these carers are, why and how they become carers and what the effects of caring are on them before we can look at strategies which may 'empower' them.

There is a high expectation amongst the general population that families (mostly married daughters and spouses) should care for dependent older people – and indeed they do. The vast majority of dependent older people either live with someone else or say they are visited by a relative several times a week. 4.5 million carers provide some sort of regular care for older people and one million carers provide more than 20 hours a week.

Carers are part of care by the community, a service predominantly by women for older women. Whether someone is likely to become a carer is affected by the presence and availability of other relatives, gender, emotional closeness, culture and race and geographical distance. Spouses care in preference to children, children in preference to other relations and other relations before non-relations. Having said that, over 30% of carers are men, mostly spouses and unmarried sons. The proportion of husbands and wives who care are roughly equal. Three times more daughters (and daughters-in-law) care in preference to sons.

It is often within three generational relationships that the carer finds herself with conflicting demands from husbands, children and parents. The woman may be in paid work or have just started to go back to work after staying at home for many years. In either case, the pressure on her to give up work is immense. Sons may also have conflicts between caring and work, but this is more likely to be recognised by statutory services (Levin et al 1989).

41

In relation to geographical distance, a son living with his mother may provide care in preference to a daughter who lives some distance away, and those living two hours travelling time away or more are virtually prevented from providing care.

One in eight carers are more distantly related, but are caring because of a longstanding close relationship with the older person (Levin et al 1989). This may of course include unrecognised 'spouses' because they are the same sex as the cared for person.

Relatives 'drift' into caring as a kind of natural progression from an already existing relationship or slip into it because of affection, duty or obligation. Those relationships arising out of a sense of obligation can be highly stressful for both parties. All caring relationships are open-ended, with no predictability about if or when the state will step in. These stresses may lead to abuse by the carer or the cared for person. As will be seen in Chapter 7 when considering people with dementia, the stress suffered by the carer may be especially acute.

Those who feel most responsible are most likely to shoulder the most burden. Even within a household, one person is likely to take on the principal caring role; for example, in a study of older people with married couples living nearby, the woman provided 191 minutes a day of care and the men 13 minutes (Nissel and Bonnerjea 1982).

Young Carers

The obligation to care is particularly poignant when that carer is a child. They may, rarely, be carers of grandparents, but workers need to be aware of this possibility. Children's and young people's needs have been either invisible and, when known about, not seen as a priority by statutory bodies. It is known that they feel unable to ask for help even if they feel they need it. This is partly because of stigma, but also because of their fear of the family breaking up. A recent survey of local authorities found that many had no processes in place to find out about young carers, nor to provide support and relief from caring, if that is what they want (Dearden et al 1995).

In conclusion, whether unpaid relatives look after older dependent people depends on a number of factors which affect the relationship and therefore the needs of the carer.

Friends and Neighbours

In addition to relatives as carers, there are other networks made up of friends, neighbours, church and societies. Neighbours are often involved in practical caring tasks, such as shopping, helping with maintenance of house or garden, giving lifts and so on, but are rarely involved in personal caring tasks. It seems that they are more likely to help out if families are supporting the older person. They are less likely to help when they are apprehensive of having to bear the responsibility of caring alone, because they may be 'trapped' into providing more and more care. Their support can therefore be seen as complementary to personal care provided by relatives.

The Impact of Caring on Carers

As we have already said, the impact of the caring role depends on how it came about and the relationship between the carer and cared for person. About 10% of carers interviewed in one study of the general population said they definitely wanted to give up caring (Nissel and Bonnerjea 1982). The more distant the relationship the better was the mental health of the carer. Studies of relatives providing a great deal of care suggest both the physical and mental health of a large proportion of carers is affected.

There appear to be the following sources of stresses on carers:

- **Practical** – this would include lifting people, providing personal care, washing clothes, and so on:

    "Not only may these tasks be exhausting and distressing in themselves but they reduce the time for other things, thereby adding to the carer's sense of rush and conflicting demands."

- **Behavioural** – the cared for person may resent the enforced dependency and be resentful and sometimes violent. If, in addition, they are suffering from confusion:

    "they may wander, forget to light the gas, or repeatedly ask the same questions. They can frighten through aggression, exhaust by waking the carer in the night, and so on."

- **Interpersonal** – The caring task can erode the relationship which existed before. Others grieve for the virtual loss of the person they knew.

- **Social** – time required by care giving can erode the opportunities for a social life. It can restrict going out and keeping in touch with friends; can restrict the ability to take holidays or take paid work (Levin et al 1989).

In addition, caring also penalises carers financially as care allowances do not compensate for the necessary expenses. For women of working age, there will be an immediate loss of income if they have to give up work, affecting also their entitlement to a pension. Young carers are often isolated; their emotional needs are sometimes unmet and they can miss out on schooling.

Where the only option is depending on a relative, the caring relationship can be quite exploitative. Whilst this may not always be the case – many carers feel positive about their caring role – caring for is not the same thing as caring about and many dependent people prefer that existing reciprocal emotional and social relationships with spouses and children continue as before, with the physical care being given by paid carers.

The wife of a man who became disabled through Parkinson's Disease described how she gradually had to give more and more of her life over to caring for her husband, eventually giving up an interesting and well paid job. The only relief she has is when children provide either a few hours or the odd week when she can go away. She is no longer able to see her husband as an emotional support and describes how she has had to divorce herself emotionally from him in order to continue care – "it's just a job". The losses for her have been enormous – loss of self-esteem and financial reward gained through paid work, loss of an intimate relationship, the stress of physical caring. She has no help from the formal sector, apart from a weekly visit from a district nurse. She knows that there are tremendous financial demands on social services and feels that while she can cope, she will do so. She has some help from a sitting service once a week when she is involved in a carers support group. In any case, her husband does not want anyone except the family to look after him.

Carers often do not ask for help in the caring task until some crisis occurs either for themselves or the cared-for person.

Ethnicity

Racism leads planners and workers to have a number of erroneous assumptions about black families, such as the stereotype that they will look after their own relatives. In fact, whether there are relatives who are able to care for their elders depends on the position of different minority ethnic groups. For example, in one study of 400 older people (Bhalla and Blakemore 1981):

> "one-third of the Asian respondents and one half of the African-Caribbean respondents had no family in the neighbourhood. 25% of the Asian respondents had no family in Britain".

Progressive tightening of immigration rules mean that family reunification is no longer seen as a real possibility and elders may be isolated. The pool of carers is therefore likely to be drawn from a growing pool of over-50s. Carers may need support services to help them to continue to care, although this might be somewhat difficult for them to accept.

Not much is known about the contribution to care of neighbours and friends. Only 5% of Bhalla and Blakemore's sample were looked after by neighbours on discharge from hospital – for white people it was 11%. On the other hand 95% were looked after by relatives – for white people it was 75%. African-Caribbean families have expressed fears about whether their children will be willing to look after them.

Carers from minority ethnic groups may feel unable to ask for help from statutory services for the same reasons as those they care for (see Chapter 3). When some black people do telephone statutory services, they may be deterred by a hostile or uncomprehending response from those who answer the telephone. Elders may feel ashamed that their children cannot look after them and in any case may feel that services may not meet their cultural needs.

Lack of demand is taken to be lack of need and reinforces existing stereotypical views.

Empowerment

The role of the statutory sector

What is the role of local authorities and health services in relation to the needs of carers? There are two separate issues here. One relates to the needs of the older dependent person and the other relates to the needs of carers themselves, so that they can carry on with their caring role if they wish to. Both of these aspects need workers to negotiate a solution to either the service-user's or carer's needs. It is hard in any case to divorce the two sets of needs.

Carers' need for information about services for the people they care for

We have already said that carers, whether they are directly caring for a dependent elderly relative, friend or neighbour or not, may be interested and involved to a greater or lesser extent in their future care.

Whether they live nearby or far away, it is therefore important for carers to have as much information as possible about services which may meet the service-user's needs in order to be able to be effective partners with service-users and professional workers. As we have said in other chapters, this information needs to be in a form which is understandable and readily available to all communities and people with particular communication difficulties. If carers do not have accurate information, they can inadvertently undermine information given to the service-user by health, housing, social services and voluntary sector workers.

In addition to information that anyone needs in order to access services (Chapters 3 and 4), carers specifically need to know:

- what effect service-user's physical or mental condition will have on their ability to cope now and in the future;

- what the rights of people needing continuing medical care are, so that they can negotiate from a position of knowledge. They may find themselves having to advocate for those unable or unwilling to speak on their own behalf;

- what equipment is available to enable the cared- for person to be as independent as possible and, if the carer is providing direct care, how does the equipment work. They will need instructions about the use and maintenance of hoists, wheelchairs, walking frames, hearing aids, continence aids, etc. from health and social services specialists;
- what welfare benefits there are for service-users with care needs and their carers;
- what support groups there are for people suffering from particular conditions. There are many voluntary organisations who can support the service-user and carer with information, day services, holidays and so on;
- within any service provided, how much the carer will be able to be involved.

Carers may want to be involved with the cared-for person in exploring possible choices and need to be empowered to do so. If the cared-for person wishes, carers can accompany them when they visit services independent of statutory workers.

It is only when carers have as much information as possible that they can feel they can share in the decision-making processes necessary to meet their cared-for person's needs.

Working with risk and conflict of opinion

The deterioration of the independence of a close relative or friend is very anxiety-provoking and can lead to conflicts of opinion about what should happen. This might stem from anxiety about risk, or burn-out from caring leading to the carer wishing to give up their role and to 'persuade' the person that their best interests lie in entering residential or nursing care.

If the carer and cared-for person disagree about how the person's needs can be met, the worker must be skilled at enabling everyone to deal with the conflict and negotiate a solution which, if possible, takes account of carers' and service-users' needs. Carers need to be involved in the assessment and management of risk with the service-user who, if they are able to do so, will sometimes prefer to choose

47

to live at risk at home. Even in the case of someone with dementia, we know that if it is possible to enable that person to stay in familiar surroundings for as long as possible, they are less likely to become disorientated and deteriorate in their mental health, even if they are at some physical risk.

In order to understand why a carer may disagree with the cared-for person about their care, it is important for the worker to see the carer as separate. Any hidden conflict may sabotage any package of care.

Carers and the people they care for are more likely to feel in control of what is happening, the more that they understand the risk involved within different choices and are involved in the processes involved in coming to a decision.

If everyone decides that the best way to meet the cared for person's needs is through residential care, great care must be taken by everyone concerned, when plans are being made, to continue to value the carer's input. Carers need to know that they are still seen as essential to that person's life and that they can continue to provide care in the residential or nursing home, take the person out for visits, be involved in fund-raising and so on, if and when they wish to do so. They may need emotional support through the loss of the caring role. Carers are concerned about the quality of care that is being given to the person they have been caring for over a long period of time. Residents and carers groups can work together with staff to set standards of care for the home.

Emergencies

Families often approach statutory services at a time of crisis, when the main carer becomes physically or mentally ill. It is very worrying and disempowering for everyone concerned if no contingency plans have been made beforehand. Workers should therefore, when assessing the needs of the cared for person, discuss with both parties what they would like to happen in the event of the unforeseen temporary absence of the carer. In order for someone to step in smoothly, all the cared-for person's needs should be recorded, including those met by unpaid carers. The contingency plans and these needs should be recorded on the care plan.

Enabling Carers to Care in Their Way

Carers have needs of their own which arise out of being a carer, but which are separate from the needs of the one being cared for and require separate attention. Assessors need to respect that the carer must have varying time for themselves in order to fulfil their own needs and so as not to become exhausted. Carers need to be enabled to define how they would like to have their needs for support met, leading to a sharing of care if that will enable them to carry on with their caring role.

Information

In order to empower carers, the kind of information they may need in order to be able to choose solutions to their needs may be:

- what the eligibility criteria are in relation to their cared-for person, which will then apply to their own situation;

- how to access their own assessment;

- what kinds of services there are to meet their needs, including their need for a variety of breaks from caring;

- what carers' support groups there are.

Choice

In order to enable carers to be in control as much as is possible, they need to know what all the choices are and what the implications are socially, physically, emotionally and financially for themselves. They also need to know what backup they will have in their own caring role.

Carers may have found that as the care task becomes more and more demanding, they are no longer able to lead the life they need or want to. They may find tasks such shopping, visiting friends, going to church or mosque, visiting the dentist and so on, more and more difficult. Any longer break to visit distant friends and relatives or go on holiday may seem impossible. Carers need to be offered as much flexibility as possible to lead a relatively normal life.

Mrs Smith lives with her son and daughter-in-law. Mrs S's health was fine when she came to live there, but gradually her health has deteriorated. Her daughter-in-law works part-time and wishes to continue to do so. They have never got on particularly well and her daughter-in-law is happy enough to provide non-personal tasks, but does not want to provide personal care. Mrs S has fallen a few times and her daughter-in-law thinks she is no longer able to live with her and should go into residential care. Mrs S is adamant that she wants to stay at home. The GP and social worker worked together with Mrs S and her daughter-in-law to work out a solution which included sharing the care between the daughter-in-law and the day centre so that she was able to have time for herself and her husband.

The ideal here is to 'give' them a number of hours or days per month and contract with a provider on their behalf to provide flexible opportunities within this negotiated time. Any agreement about the carer's needs should be recorded, whether it is in joint documentation or separately.

Interpersonal Skills

Great skill is needed to negotiate with existing unpaid carers. Assumptions and judgments can be made about the willingness of relatives and neighbours to care, but people must never be expected to care against their will. Situations can be complex and carers need to have the opportunity to express their conflicting and changing feelings. Negotiations must be done in such a way that it complements or supplements care according to the wishes of carer and the cared-for person. The carer will probably be asking for help at a time of crisis, in the knowledge that she or he and the cared-for person will be giving up their independence by asking for help. They may fear that they will not receive any help in any case, or feel ashamed that they can no longer cope. They may be grieving for the losses experienced by the cared-for person, and possibly for the change in their own relationship if it is a partnership, especially if the person is suffering from dementia. They may have more than one caring role plus outside work, some or all of which conflict. There may be relationship problems, either longstanding or recent. Workers need to give carers time to work through these conflicts and changes.

People may not want anyone else to care for them and skills are needed to enable them to understand the need for the unpaid carer to have some breaks from caring. They may not trust anyone else to carry out personal care tasks and time needs to be spent building up trust between them and paid carers.

Meeting carers' needs when the caring situation is breaking down

Sometimes the caring situation becomes intolerable, leading to feelings of resentment, anger, stress, powerlessness and guilt. Workers need to be sensitive to signs of stress which may, in the long run, lead to abuse either by the carer or by the cared-for person. This may occur because of the dependency of the carer on the cared-for person, for example, for housing or emotional support. It may be because of stress factors such as chronic financial stress, or a bereavement, or because the older person and their carer are isolated within the caring relationship. There may be little opportunity for either of them to have an outside life or any relief from each other. It may be that their relationship has always been abusive and this has continued into old age. The carer may have a mental disorder or be a heavy drug or alcohol user. We do not intend to go into the complexities of abuse here except to say that the carer (and service-user), whether legal action is contemplated or not, will need understanding and assistance. Where the abused person wishes to continue living with the other person, if they have an assessment of their own needs, the stress may be taken out of the situation and abuse often lessens or ceases. This work needs a knowledge of inter-agency policy and procedures.

If the conflict between the service-user and carer is too great for one person to deal with, a separate advocate or assessor may be needed to represent the carer's needs.

Self-help and advocacy

Some carers find that they receive great comfort from meeting other carers in similar situations and will use their opportunities to meet up with them. This empowers them by reducing the feelings of isolation and by the sharing of information about ways of coping.

Carers' groups can also advocate for the needs of carers and can assist individual carers to identify their own needs separately from the needs of the cared-for person.

Involvement in policy-making, planning and training

Carers need to be empowered to contribute to planning and policy-making so that services are sensitive to their needs. At a strategic level, carers groups and their representatives need to be actively involved on any planning group. At a local level, again carers should be involved in planning services for themselves. Carers and service-users can come together within residential and day services to be involved in planning on a day-to-day level.

Carers need to be involved in training for paid carers, both as participants and trainers. This needs careful planning and preparation of the carers and other participants. Carers as trainers need to be paid and cover provided while they are involved.

Conclusion

Work with carers can be very challenging. It is not easy for workers to empower both carers and the person being cared for. The principles of working in partnership with carers are essential in order to support them in whichever way they choose.

Chapter Seven

People with Dementia – Standing in Their Shoes

Introduction

Much of what we talk about in this book, in particular about the assessment and care management process, will apply to individuals suffering from dementia. In this chapter, we will focus on some issues which relate particularly to empowering people who are affected by dementia and also relate to empowering their carers.

Definition of Dementia

Dementia is the main organic mental disorder in older people. It affects parts of the brain, thereby affecting memory, the capacity to solve the problems of day-to-day living, the performance of social skills and control of emotional reactions.

There are two main types of dementia – senile dementia of the Alzheimer type which is a disease of the brain and is difficult to diagnose, and multi-infarct dementia which is caused by a series of small strokes. In addition there is dementia associated with Parkinson's disease, head injury, alcohol and more recently with AIDS.

Dementia is not the confusion caused by conditions which are treatable, such as infections and depression.

Stages of Dementia

The progression of dementia and the signs and symptoms vary with each individual. In the early stages it is difficult to identify and forgetfulness and a loss of ability to take in information may be put down to 'old age'. Relatives may gradually compensate for these losses of ability without really noticing and it is not until their support is lost through illness or accident that the full extent of these losses is noticed by others. In the so-called middle stages, these abilities continue to deteriorate and severe mistakes can be made, such as forgetting to light the gas. People may lose their way when they are talking and be unable to remember the meaning of words; they may forget what has just happened, but still remember the past clearly; they may forget the use of objects. Eventually, they may be unable to carry out self-care tasks and lose control of bowel movements. They may repeat behaviour obsessionally. There is no cure or treatment for dementia as such, although symptoms may be treated. Thinking about dementia in stages has limited use, however, when it comes to meeting individual needs.

Prevalence of Dementia

This is very difficult to ascertain as studies use different measures to find out how many people suffer from dementia. Average figures show that about 3% of those over 65 may have dementia, 20% of those over 75, and 25% of those over 85 may suffer from dementia.

Disempowerment

Stereotyping – what happens when individual needs are invisible because assumptions are made?

When people's mental ability to reason and communicate and decide has been impaired, they can feel, and be, very disempowered. Ageism already means that older people are not seen as having the power to control their own lives.

Some people with dementia describe themselves as experiencing an overwhelming feeling of fear and anxiety. Others seem to cope with the experience better. A lack of understanding and respect from others may add to these feelings, producing behaviour such as aggression – which is often seen as caused by the illness, rather than an understandable reaction to people's lack of empathy. 'Wandering' may or may not be purposeful, but again may be seen as a symptom and treated with drugs, rather than something which may be explicable by understanding the person's past occupation in their present behaviour. Some behaviour may remain inexplicable.

The behaviour resulting from the effects of dementia, such as hesitant and confused speech and 'unexplainable' and erratic behaviour, can lead people around them to find it difficult to imagine that they are capable of having any control over their own lives. People may put any different behaviour down to 'just old age' or 'you cannot do anything – they're confused'. Their relatives may take them over, making decisions 'for the best' for them, without taking into account their own wishes.

Paid carers may concentrate on the purely physical processes of protecting people from risk and keeping bodies clean and fed. They may make assumptions that a person with dementia has no individuality or any social, emotional or sexual needs – that all people with dementia are the same.

Workers may find it testing, working with those with dementia, for a number of reasons. They may fear becoming old and affected by

54

dementia themselves. It may be difficult to be patient with people who may constantly repeat themselves and who may be so frustrated that they express this through hitting, spitting and so on. Because of differing values and attitudes found among staff, the person with dementia may find that workers react inconsistently, furthering their feeling of confusion and disempowerment.

Empowerment

Because of what we know about how easily people with dementia can be disempowered, it is essential that unpaid carers, carers and other staff not only understand the causes of confusion and dementia but also work hard to enable older people with dementia to have as much say in their lives as possible and to continue to live as they always have done.

Values – working with individuals

Basic human values, such as dignity, respect for the person, individuality, independence, privacy, occupation, equal opportunities and choice to live in the way that they wish, are a core part of work with all people. Ensuring that these values are translated into practice when working with older people with dementia is even more essential when those people find it difficult or impossible to express their wishes.

Workers need to be aware of how their values are translated through the tone of voice or through body language.

They need to keep in mind that the person does have their own individual needs and wishes, including a need to be understood as someone with feelings – emotional needs – as well as a need for meaningful occupation within their capabilities and understanding.

Information giving and gathering – what do workers need to focus on?

Assessment

Finding out information which will enable a person to continue to live their lives in a meaningful way will often be a case of trial and error. Those gathering information will not have the usual safeguard of being able to check that the person wants information about their past lives gathered, as it is often done through a third party.

To find out how a person would want to live their life, workers may:

- use their powers of observation, noticing such things as photographs and the person's environment. This may tell the assessor about the person's state of health;

- work with those who care enough about the person to express their wishes without distorting them. Those closest to the person may be able to give a worker information about their past and present likes and dislikes, information about the way they have lived their lives, including their family, work and social networks and structures. This may be a relative and/or close friend. It may also be a paid carer, or general practitioner who has provided care for them for a long time;

- use such techniques as life story work with the person with dementia in order to assess needs and the coping mechanisms of that person.

Risk Assessment

Assessors will need to assess risk and take steps to lessen that risk alongside others who know them well. People with dementia may be unable to recognise the risks. However, they are often able to co-operate with risk reduction measures and are able to live at an acceptably safe level. Assessment of people's ability to look after their own financial matters will also have to be carried out. In exceptional circumstances, assessment of risk under the Mental Health Act 1983 and theNational Assistance Act 1948 may be undertaken.

Mrs S gradually became more confused at home, and one day her daughter visited as usual and smelt gas. To her horror, her mother had left the gas stove on. She talked to the social worker and together they worked out a plan to lessen the risk by disconnecting the stove and by the daughter and Meals on Wheels providing ready prepared meals. This danger had to be balanced against the loss of skill and normality experienced by Mrs S in order for her to remain at home

Working with Carers

In addition to the ways of working with family and friends mentioned in Chapter 6:

- workers need to empower unpaid carers to express their feelings about their situation. They may have chosen to look after the person with dementia, but they may not have done so and may resent the role;

- carers may need information about dementia and its effects so as to enable them to understand what is happening in order that they can help the cared-for person understand as much as possible;

- relatives and friends may be unable to cope with the gradual loss of the person they have known, or with the risks they see the person face in their daily life;

- they may need a break from caring, which the cared-for person does not want and is not able to recognise at all. This will need skilled intervention, working with both people, in order for a break to be possible;

- relatives may need support to help them cope with the feelings that result from struggling to care for the person with dementia. That support will need to continue once they recognise that they can no longer cope on their own, or that the person has to go into residential or nursing home care;

- carers may get support through carers groups supported by Age Concern, Alzheimer's Disease Society and carers associations, as well as in day services and residential homes.

Time

Communicating with and understanding the needs and wishes of people with dementia takes time. Workers need to get to know well the person and their family, friends and neighbours in order to be trusted and to understand the hopes and fears of each person and the dynamics between them. Carers may need time to talk about their feelings of grief and guilt.

The person may have times when they are able to think and communicate more clearly, and it is important for workers to respect this and to spend enough time with them at different times of the day to find out when this is or to listen to those who may know.

Both the person and the worker may find it less tiring to restrict the time of visits and break up the process of getting to know someone into manageable chunks of time. Even if emergency services have to be provided in order to make someone safe, assessors and carers need to continue the process of taking time to get to know the person.

Paid carers need to take time to respond to any signs of distress, such as anger, tears, and agitation. Sometimes these signs are the only way people have of showing that they are not all right. They also need to take time to find out how to meet people's need for stimulation and company or solitude – this may have to be through a process of trial and error.

Enabling people to retain and regain skills

Life story books can record important events in the person's past, which will remind themselves of their past lives. Because people with dementia will often remember and sometimes live in the past, and may lose last those skills they gained when they were younger, it is important to know what they could and can do, so as keep those skills going for as long as is possible. However, information gatherers need to be extremely careful about collecting together photographs and documentation from the past. There may be information about the past they would prefer not to be widely shared.

Choice of where people live?

Every effort must be made to make it clear to the person what choices they may have about where they live and who might look after them. Their wishes must be taken into account as much as is possible. Many with dementia do best by remaining in familiar surroundings. If this is not possible, residential homes with staff who are trained to work with people with dementia is a good substitute providing the person's room can have familiar furniture and belongings in it. Special needs units may be able to meet the needs of those people with behavioural difficulties. However, where behaviour is extremely challenging and in the terminal stages of dementia, people may have their needs best met in specialist nursing homes.

Transition – how can workers help people to move from their own environment to a strange place?

We know that moving can be disturbing for anyone. For people with dementia, this can be extremely disorientating and add to their confusion. Life story work can prepare them to move from one environment to another, whether on a short-term basis to hospital or to give a carer a short break, or to move permanently into care.

For example, photographs can be taken of the places in which they lived if they still exist, where they live now, and where they will be moving to. Familiar possessions can be taken with them, such as books, a radio, tapes, knickknacks, hobbies and the results of hobbies, photographs of close relatives and friends, including familiar paid domiciliary carers. For a more permanent move, they can take furniture and pets.

Information on the care plan – what kind of detail is needed for those unable to communicate well for themselves?

In addition to the usual kind of information on a care plan, special care needs to be taken:

- to record needs in detail and the ways in which they might be met. Again, the information gained through the biographical or life story approach is useful in order to give carers a good picture of the person in their past as well as in their present.

- to tell carers about the possible behavioural effects of dementia and the medication used to treat some of the symptoms.

Provision of Care

Orientation and reminiscence

Those living with people with dementia need to give them information about the world about them, including such things as the time of day, day and date, including significant dates, such as birthdays, festivals, etc. Visual clues to their environment such as labels and charts, photographs, colours and textures help people to retain their sense of space and structure within their own home and especially in institutional buildings, and can lessen confusion.

Workers can help empower people by listening to stories of the past. They can bring memorabilia or music from people's past to the individual or group, so as to stimulate memories. It is necessary for workers to be aware of possible repercussions of reminding people of their past and to know how to deal with anxiety or grief which may be stirred up. People may be living in very distressing pasts that could include war or abuse.

Interpersonal skills

The same basic skills of communication need to be used whether or not there is dementia. However, there are additional difficulties.

Communication breaks down gradually as dementia progresses. In the early stages, communication may only be marginally affected, such as not being able to get to the point easily, not understanding jargon and sarcasm, not being able to concentrate for long on what they are saying. They may complain of being unable to find words and use words which are more general.

In some social situations, some individuals are skilled at the superficiality of a conversation (confabulation) and people can be deceived about the extent of dementia. As people's abilities deteriorate, they may repeat ideas which are limited and may rely on remembrance of past happenings. They may lose the ability to name objects. Finally, people may be unaware of meaning and little of what they say is relevant to the situation. They may not be able to produce related ideas and may repeat words meaninglessly. The facial expression is often not the same as what the individual is saying; a listener may have to listen carefully and check for understanding.

Where people's first language is not English, they will tend to lose use of English and revert to the language of their childhood.

> Mr B came to England from Pakistan in the early 1950s. He successfully ran his own business and became fluent in English. More recently he suffered from dementia which meant that eventually he went to live in a residential home. The majority of residents and staff are white. Mr B uses English less and less

often and some of the staff think he is just being awkward by refusing to speak English. Mr B is distressed and shows this by withdrawing into himself, but occasionally he tries to hit out at staff. The residential home's manager decides to tell the assessor that Mr B is in the wrong place. Once she and the staff realised that Mr B was actually losing his English because of his disease, they were able to respond to him appropriately rather than in a racist way.

Communication

So, what do workers need to do to be as successful as possible in communicating with and understanding those with dementia? Firstly, it is important to get to know the person well and for the worker to be trusted. The person may forget who the worker is, so that she or he will always have to take time to build the relationship again.

Any worker should:

- always include the person in any conversation that concerns them;
- check that the person has their hearing aid, glasses and dentures;
- try to talk to people in a quiet environment. Television, radio noise and other conversations can be distracting.

They should

- be aware that feelings will be conveyed through the use of words – for example, speed, tone and pitch, always speak normally and do not talk down, speak loudly and clearly but do not shout;
- make sure before they speak that the person's attention has been gained by putting themselves in the person's line of attention, making sure they have eye contact and perhaps by greeting the person by introducing themselves – "It's Judy";
- make sure their facial expression and body match what they are saying;
- check before they touch anyone whether it is welcome or not, as it could be seen as threatening;

- keep what they say short and give one piece of information at a time;

- link what the person has done before with the present, e.g. do you remember when you did . . .? Well, now we are going to do it again, – or – this time we will do something slightly differently.

- only give two choices and not more, e.g. do you want porridge or toast?

- not ask open questions, e.g. What do you want for breakfast? This does not give any clues.

Workers must

- always check that they have understood what the individual is saying, e.g. Do you mean that you want toast today and that you want jam on it? Look for signs of agreement or dissent;

- use hands, arms and body to emphasise what they are saying.

Whatever people say, workers need to concentrate on their feelings and react to those (validation). For example, "I want mother" could indicate that the person is feeling lonely or that no one cares about them. They need to be aware of when someone is trying to communicate with them by sounds or gestures.

However difficult communication is, the attitude of the listener must still be one of seeing the person as an individual, treating them with respect and being non-judgmental.

Environmental effects on behaviour

The effect of dementia on people is different for each individual. The behaviour may stem from a variety of causes including the attitudes and actions of other people and the actual physical environment, as well as from the feelings and frustrations of the person with dementia.

Defining behaviour as 'aggression' or 'wandering' is not necessarily helpful. Workers need to be a lot more precise than this and find out what might have caused the behaviour. They will need to know what the person's background is and whether their behaviour has always been there. For example, the person may always have been violent and aggressive towards women. Workers will also need to know something about the occupation of the person; for example, a woman who always becomes agitated at about 3.00pm may be imagining that she has to fetch her child from school. There may have been an action or attitude by staff which caused the behaviour.

A new resident was walking along the corridor and suddenly hit out at a passing member of staff. He said he wanted to go home. The carer was concerned but in rather a hurry, so she responded by telling him that he would get used to the place soon; after all, it was very nice and friendly. He was not comforted and started sobbing and shouting that he wanted to leave. The key worker told her later that the resident had not been told the truth about coming to the home for good. The care team met to discuss a plan of action which included encouraging the resident's daughter to tell him the truth and to support the resident and daughter through their bereavement. The daughter was reluctant to do this because she did not want to hurt his feelings but when she was supported to do so, her father was able to grieve for the loss of his independent life in his own home and gradually settled into the home.

The questions which need to be asked when a person is expressing themselves in a way which is 'challenging' include:

- "What exactly happened?"
- "When and where did it happen?"
- "How long has it being going on for?"
- "What else was happening?"
- "Who else was involved?"

Staff then need to be able to describe the behaviour itself.

They then need to describe the consequences of the behaviour. They need to ask, "Who is this a problem for?" For instance, it may be a problem for the person themselves in terms of risk of hurting themselves, or other residents or staff may be at risk. Each of these answers will require different actions.

Did the person receive more attention as a result of the behaviour? This may be a clue to the fact that the person is suffering from a lack of attention or is bored or upset. Trial and error is necessary in order to find solutions to the person's behaviour.

Conclusion

People with dementia need as much reassurance and consistency as possible. They need to be listened to carefully, to what they are saying both verbally and non-verbally. Above all, staff need to empower them to retain their dignity and independence as much as is possible through the use of active listening and empathy.

Chapter Eight

Negotiating for a Better Quality of Life

A lot of emphasis is placed on assessment by those who carry it out – who should do it, how, what is a needs assessment? And rightly so. Without a 'good' assessment, no relationship has been formed which empowers the person to state their difficulties, nor can they begin together to work towards solutions.

Of course, assessment in itself is of limited value. On its own it does not enable the identified needs to be met, though it will have helped the person acknowledge and explore their needs.

Care planning, implementation of the care plan, and monitoring/ review are the other three main components of the care management process. It is here that the agreements of the service-user and the assessor come to the service-provider for the needs to be met and where this new situation is then checked to ensure the 'right fit', and best outcome.

And, like all bureaucratic processes, it requires care for the person, who understands little of the jargon or the intention behind it, to feel in control of what is happening.

Care Planning

In the book *'More Power to Our Elders'*, Jef Smith says:

"The role of the assessor is to help the client to make her own calculation of the elements of life which are of most importance to her, and of the style of care which will best protect her chosen lifestyle". (Hobman et al 1994)

Care planning is one of the most challenging parts of the process for the assessor. It is where principles about 'choice' and 'respecting preferences' are put to the test. Yet despite this, it is not unknown for assessors, albeit in jest, to express to colleagues exasperation that such and such a person has decided not to go to the day centre after all. What a nuisance! Perhaps this was because needs had not been adequately broken down – a detailed understanding has to be achieved if needs are to be met in an appropriate way. For example, loneliness might not best be resolved by attendance at a day centre. Counselling may be required to accept bereavement or assistance required to renew old contacts.

And yet, the most remarkable thing is that most people will settle well into services if the assessor has understood the needs, enabled choice to be expressed and empowered the person to try a few different things out before making a final decision. The final care plan has to be negotiated. It may not always be obvious at first what exactly will meet the needs. Moreover, people need to understand what services might be on offer, what is affordable and what compromises might need to be made.

... a woman about to be discharged from hospital alleged that she was taken to see a residential home without being told. . .

"I was told it was a home visit and I assumed I was going to my home", said the client. (Age Concern 1995)

Care planning is a skilled task, but it is hard to find excuses for the situation outlined above. What might have allowed that to occur? Time pressures, perhaps; pressure from the hospital to release the bed, maybe; a lack of regard for the rights of an older person, certainly.

No two people will have the same care plan, unless it is of the most simple kind, any more than they will have exactly the same clothes in their wardrobe. A true tailor-made care plan reflects personality, motivation, lifestyle and many other undefinable aspects, if it is to meet individual need. It must build on strengths and try to support normal life activity and networks. This principle must underlie the care plan, even if it is complex and requires input by many different agencies.

At this initial stage, many people will lack information about available options and will need frank discussion about these and possible costs. If the resource is not within their own home, they will need to visit and spend time in day centres, different Homes and so on. The assessor must have regard for their fear and anxiety in this process, as must their hosts for the day.

Where a person has dementia, as discussed in Chapter 7, options are more difficult to present verbally. Time and observation will be required. The attitude of 'she wouldn't know a residential home from the beach at Blackpool, so doesn't need to visit' is unlikely to result in a person getting the very best from their new environment.

For people whose requirements are felt to be 'different', everyday concerns will be doubled. Can they rely on the assessor to convey to potential providers any religious practices; what about food; will there be anyone with a similar life experience to talk to? If they are from an ethnic minority group, they may fear encountering racism. It is obviously for providers to ensure that their services can meet the needs of all members of the community. However, at the care planning stage the assessor will need to empower the older person to talk over specific needs.

Carers' needs will also need to be taken into account. Careful negotiation may be necessary to meet the needs of the one without abusing the rights of the other. Where dementia or another condition makes communication difficult, it is tempting to meet the needs of the more articulate carer at a cost to the service-user.

Care planning is a complex process. Time spent at this stage will enable the individual to feel as much in control as possible. Even if services have to be arranged in an emergency, they should be seen as provisional until the person has been able to think through their needs and what choices are available.

Implementing the Care Plan

Once decisions have been made, the care plan can be finalised and implemented by making agreements with service-providers.

At this stage, the service-user may feel completely alone, vulnerable and powerless. Having agreed a certain course of action, the named assessor may appear to fade from the picture, leaving the service-user to accept, for example, a stranger in their home to assist with personal care. She may find herself alone all day amongst a dozen other people whom she has never met before. The reality of their vulnerability, especially if this is the first time they have had to accept services, may strike home.

The sensitivity of the new provider is important here. Such feelings could have been minimised by careful introductions. If going to a day centre or residential home is planned, it can help for a care assistant to visit the person in their own home, to create a good link between home and service. If there has not been time for proper introductions or the information has not been particularly detailed, special effort will be required to help the new service-user to adjust. We all know what it is like to experience new situations which may not be what we would overall have preferred and the attentiveness which this awareness brings will help ease the situation.

A Hindu woman did not eat beef or like to eat pork. Meals services regularly sent meals containing these meats. Due to language differences she was unable to contact the organisers to explain or complain. She was however quite happy to receive 'Western' type meals without beef or pork.

The named assessor has no doubt gone to work with other people, but the needs of their service-user at this stage must not be pushed to the bottom of their priorities. Complex care plans are often shaky at first and the named assessor, by checking out early in the implementation how the person is finding it, can make any adjustments necessary. This will result in enabling the person to feel in control – otherwise they may take the easier route of grateful compliance or depression, for lack of anyone to talk things over with.

Monitoring and Review

It takes a while to know if the services are going to meet the need and to see if they are going to suit the person. Early anxiety will give way to familiarity; alternatively, any honeymoon period will be overtaken by reality. Various changes may need to be made to ensure the care package suits and it is important that everyone involved in the first weeks remain sensitive to the possible need for adjustment or even radical change. It is helpful to the person if one of the people providing the service has a special responsibility in this, a 'keyworker' role, to monitor and advocate if the care plan is not working quite right.

It is important that the named assessor arranges a specific time when they will sit down with the person to look at how everything is going, giving plenty of opportunities for carers or advocates to be present if the person chooses, but avoiding the disempowering effects of too many people. Keyworkers can help here in encouraging those whose memory is not good or who find such occasions difficult to write things down or to make other preparations. The more the named assessor views this process as a dynamic evaluation of what is happening rather than a rather low-key routine, the more they will seek opportunities to make it a worthwhile event for the service-user.

The final part of this process, which is not along a straight line but rather a never-ending cycle of reassessment, revision of care plan and review, is for the assessor to feed up to those responsible for planning the needs which have not been met and the compromises which have had to be made. Empowerment is not only about having one's own needs met in the way one prefers and chooses, but is about knowing that one's experience will assist future developments.

Chapter Nine

'Normal Life' at Home

Empowerment Issues

In the first chapter, we considered briefly the history of care at home, what a new service personal care is as a domiciliary service and how it is yet to be regulated. Nevertheless, many people would consider that, if one has to receive care, then to do so at home is the very best option. It should be the ultimate empowerment strategy. There is no need to uproot; one remains 'in control' rather than having to fit in with institutional routines; a person retains all their familiar possessions within their own house; friends, family and neighbours can pop in just as they always have done, without having to travel in a different direction or become the 'visitor' at a Home.

However, the reality is not quite so simple. Those factors may indeed exist, but other considerations can lead to a person feeling that they have very little power or control within the situation.

- *A houseful of people!* A complex care package can involve a bewildering array of people: personal carers, district nurses, specialists (e.g. physiotherapist, occupational therapist; speech therapist), the person who delivers meals, any privately-purchased help (e.g. cleaner), not to mention those whose job it is to make sure all is going well – the social worker, the GP, the manager of those providing the care etc. The 'normal' routine can be hard enough for a very frail person to manage, when perhaps 8-10 different carers a week may come into the home, but any crisis may provoke a huge influx of concerned people. Conversations about care or even about one's future can take place over a person's head. At home, where they expect to feel in charge, they are not.

- *The care management process can be disempowering.* In the chapters describing assessment and care planning, we discussed ways in which these processes can be improved upon to give people more control. Nevertheless, the harsh reality is that as things are at the moment the assessor will decide within departmental criteria what is and is not to be provided and how much time should be allocated for various tasks. At times of budget stringency, which is unfortunately all too frequent, whole services (e.g. shopping) may be withdrawn, time for personal care may be cut, new charging policies brought in. This makes the person at home feel very vulnerable – more so than their friend in residential or nursing care who, whatever happens, is unlikely to have their care provision arbitrarily changed.

- *Home care is surprisingly inflexible.* To the outsider, domiciliary care might seem the ultimate flexible system. At the care planning stage, the assessor discusses with the customer what care they need, at what time and for how long. By and large, care is provided in accordance with these preferences. But there are important exceptions – for example, it would be hard to accommodate someone who would prefer to go to bed at midnight and needs help to do so. If the person has a meal from a meals service, it will certainly be difficult to have that meal early evening, and even the lunchtime meal may not arrive at the preferred time. Bathing may 'have' to take place at 11 o'clock in the morning, because this is when the carer has a little slack time, and not at the preferred getting up and going to bed times.

- *By and large, home carers work unsupervised.* Carers go into the individual's home and complete their tasks with no manager or supervisor to hand. Where good relationships have formed, the person will have confidence in their carer and this can be one of the most successful and empowering ways of delivering care. However, the flip side of this coin is that an extremely frail or disabled person is very dependent on the carer. There may be unfortunate occasions when the carer may not turn up on time (or at all) or, hopefully, very rare times when she may be guilty of rough or disrespectful handling or may steal money or items from the home. The service-user is in a very vulnerable position, firstly, because there are no witnesses and, secondly, because of the fear that to complain might invite recriminations. Thirdly, it may not be possible to prove anything, making it all very uncomfortable. Also, as previously mentioned, domiciliary agencies are largely unregulated and contract compliance inadequately monitored.

70

Empowerment Strategies

The organisation of domiciliary care services has the potential to enable the service-user to feel on the one hand relatively in control, or on the other completely helpless. This section has, therefore, been divided into two parts – strategies for managers and strategies for carers.

Strategies for Managers

- *As in all areas of social care, information for the person is of great importance.* The assessor will already have set up the care plan, but the provider manager will need to give additional information. In general, the service-user will need to know something about the agency providing the care, who exactly will be coming to deliver care and at what times, who to contact if things are not right and how such comments will be dealt with. Much of this can and should be done by written information, but the person should also meet the manager of the carers. This will at least help them to feel more able to make contact if they are not happy with aspects of the service.

  In addition, they will need to know who is going to come in when the carer is off sick and on leave. Some of a frail person's most anxious moments occur when their carer is on leave and the substitute has not arrived at the same time. How do they know they have not been forgotten? The passing of such information requires robust systems and determination – there is a high pay-off in terms of empowerment.

- *The manager needs to keep the number of carers to a minimum.* An intensive care package could attract 42 visits a week, for example – double if two carers are required. It is a huge task for a manager to ensure that this involves the minimum of carers so that there is continuity, relationships can be formed and the person is not suffering either the indignity of having personal care from repeated new people or the tedium of explaining several times a day where things are and how things are done.

- *Matching.* The manager needs to have regard for any problems which arise between service-user and carer. This is an important

71

and intimate relationship and personality or other problems can make it an uncomfortable or unhappy experience. The manager has a responsibility to ensure a 'good match'. Sometimes, especially where issues of gender or race are involved, it is not simple – one might wish to respect a stated choice, but not, for example, if it involves racism.

- **Ensure carers know what they are doing!** Some individuals may be at such a stage of dementia that they are unable to clearly say what their care needs are. Others will have quite complex personal care needs which are hard for the person to convey. The delivery of personal care is a skilled task and, in general, carers will need to have been trained in the knowledge and attitudes necessary to achieve this successfully. Beyond this, however, when they first go into a person's home, they will need to know the purpose of the care plan and the tasks within it, and understand details relevant to that situation. There may be specific instructions from a nurse, occupational therapist or other professional. There may be specific issues relating to cultural practice; the same language may not be spoken. The individual will rapidly feel devalued and worthless if a carer arrives knowing nothing of all this.

Strategies for Carers

- **Give the person attention.** The carer is often asked to do many tasks in a brief time. It is too easy for the carer to focus on these tasks and their rapid completion rather than on the interaction with the person and the quality of the relationship with them. To receive personal care can make one feel vulnerable. At best it is an experience which empowers the person by helping them feel in control, valued and well cared for. At worst it can make them feel humiliated or that they are a nuisance. It is not easy for carers to feel confident in their own ability to deliver care successfully. They may have had very little training as the job is not commonly perceived to be a skilled one; they may not know the person or their needs very well. The attitude of the carer towards the person is therefore of vital importance – the desire to treat them with dignity and respect their privacy can overcome lacks in skill or knowledge or even time.

Such an attitude will enable a carer to use ingenuity to ensure that the time is well spent and that as much as possible they do tasks with the person and not for them. They will try not to watch the clock anxiously, even if aware that promptness provides the only hope of completing the whole workload in the time allocated. It is a lot to ask, but necessary if the service-user is to feel empowered within the service they are receiving.

- *Respect the customer's home and everything about it.* Carers who move from working in residential care to domiciliary care often comment on this notable aspect of the transition. However much staff in residential or nursing homes encourage people to feel like tenants rather than residents, few actually feel this because staff are so obviously in charge and many aspects of residential or nursing home life are out of their control. However, care given at home is very different and carers need to take account of this. Care is often difficult to deliver just because there is too much furniture lying around in the wrong places, too many bits and bobs cluttering up the work surfaces, perhaps even an ageing cat or dog defying all attempts to create a relatively hygienic environment.

  This situation simply has to be worked with and respected. The carer is a guest in the house and must continuously check out that it is all right for them to do this and use that as they move around the room and house. Any other attitude is likely to cause indignation and a loss of control which the person is unable to deal with. This is, of course, very obvious where the person is visually impaired or very confused.

- *Have regard for other family members and carers.* This respect must of course spread to any unpaid carers and other family members and friends. Carers can unwittingly get drawn into complex situations, or find themselves making judgments which do not assist the situation and sometimes out of concern deny the freedom of the individual to relate to whom they wish. Where there are unpaid carers, both parties will need support. Where there is tension, this will be increased if either one feels disempowered by the attitude of the carer.

- *Be flexible where possible.* Obviously, carers will try to work to the person's choices whenever they are delivering care or engaged in other domestic tasks. Beyond this, the carer needs to be aware of certain tensions within their situation and be able to work with them. Carers are expected to work to the care plan. This is what has been agreed to meet the assessed needs. The massive task of organising domiciliary care for many people means that there appears to be little flexibility around times. These two factors can lead to a situation where the person's general and overall needs are being met, but on any day can lead to such rigidity that other events cannot be accommodated. In order to have an element of control and continue with their own lifestyle, they need to be able to negotiate with the carer to perhaps have their visit a bit later than usual if for example the day centre has an event which keeps them late, or perhaps to use some time for a different purpose if a friend calls and helps with the tea instead of the carer. In this way, the care plan supports the person in their activities, rather than rigidly ruling the day.

- *Advocacy.* Carers do get to know their service-users very well and over time helpful relationships can build up. Sometimes these relationships are formalised into a 'keyworker' role, where it is acknowledged that the carer is able to advocate on behalf of their service-user to other professionals, including GPs, nurses and social workers. The feelings of trust which the person has in this relationship can be very empowering, especially if they have no nearby family or friends to watch out for them.

Conclusion

To date, there is very little laid down about the standard a person should expect of their domiciliary care and there is still no sign of the market being regulated. This leaves the service-user in a potentially vulnerable situation and it is only by carers and their managers clearly understanding the power that they have that they can begin to actively share it.

Chapter Ten

Choice in Day Services

Disempowering Factors

A service-led approach and a lack of information about what different day centres can offer means that day care has traditionally been rather a blunt instrument which may meet some needs but not others. In addition, members of minority ethnic groups often do not use day services because they do not know about them or do not see them as meeting their religious and cultural needs. People may not be using day services willingly, for example, if it is only arranged so that their carers can have a break during the day.

If care is not taken to match the day services available to needs, service-users may refuse to go, perhaps leaving themselves at unnecessary risk in the day. Levin et al (1989) reported that:

> "one client . . . refused or dropped out of day centres or clubs for every one who accepted them."

These people who dropped out or refused to go did so because of a lack of preparation and choice:

- it was not what they wanted in the first place;

- appropriate information was not given to them about choices;

- people do not have the chance to explore options by visiting.

At the day centre:

- attending for longer periods than they would ideally wish was exhausting;

- the activities did not suit them or were perceived as boring;

- they were put next to people with whom they had nothing in common, or who were unable to converse because of dementia or a physical impairment such as hearing loss;

- normally, most people do not spend their days with large groups of relative strangers. Not everyone likes to spend their time in groups and may be nervous about joining in;

- sometimes, in order to meet one need – loneliness or personal hygiene, for instance, the person has to take the whole package of activities provided, whether they like it or not;

It was also found that before and after attendance at the day service:

- the effort of getting ready for day care exhausts people and their carers;

- rigid transport arrangements may also mean that people may have to spend some time in transit and have to stay all day;

- transport is not suitable either because of its unreliability, or because of the discomfort experienced by some disabled people.

What exists and what do they provide?

The haphazard way in which day hospitals, voluntary lunch clubs and day centres and statutory day centres either attached to residential homes or in premises of their own, have developed means that day services are patchy and that it is difficult for people to know exactly what they offer. Which provision will meet the needs of people with dementia, people who need rehabilitation or people with a variety of religious observation and food needs is difficult to know unless the information produced by day services is available to people in the community. Again, because of the haphazardness of provision, premises, staffing and resources may prevent day services from offering all that they would want to. Day centres are sometimes, therefore, expected to do the impossible.

Empowerment

Day care offered in a host family's home, lunch clubs, day centres and day hospitals can be very popular with those who attend regularly. Many people's need for company, food and stimulation will be met there, as well as needs for care. What can workers do to empower people once they have decided that their needs may be met in this way?

In order for service-users, carers and assessors to know whether the experiencess offered in the respective day services might meet people's individual needs, the following are necessary:

Information

- day services and day hospitals need to define their own aims and objectives;

- day services and day hospitals need to have information available about times of opening, transport arrangements, flexibility and ranges of activities available so that people and their carers can absorb this at their leisure and make choices;

- information should be provided in a variety of forms so as to meet the different communication needs of the local communities;

- services need to be co-ordinated; for example, day services must be aware of other services being provided, of transport arrangements, regular outpatient appointments and regular short stays whether in hospital or residential care or hotels, in order that they can meet the needs of the individual as well as those of all service-users.

Choice

- service-users and carers need to know what choices there are to meet their needs;

- people may like the idea of day staff visiting them in their own homes or in hospital to explain what their service can and may be able to offer;

- people may be uncertain as to whether they will like going to a particular day service and need to visit a few times before deciding whether they will be happy;

- time will need to be spent by assessors and staff from day services with service-users and carers to see how that person's needs can be met in accordance with assessed needs within the care plan.

- carers and service-users who have some control over the use of a number of hours and days may choose to use them at their own convenience, not only on a regular basis but also in the case of emergencies. In order for this to happen, they need to know how to access it for themselves if they want to do so, or be clear who to approach to arrange it on their behalf.

Identifying unmet need

- day services need to respond flexibly to individual needs by developing their services and the way they are structured and run;

- staff need to be able to work alongside present and future users of services in order to identify a community's needs as well as individual needs. This will empower and enable those communities to develop facilities to meet their needs locally.

Interpersonal skills

Although people will come to a day service with an overall care plan, it may or may not include all the detailed needs of that person. Day centre workers need to spend regular time at first finding out how a person's detailed needs can be met. Carers will need to ensure that what has been agreed is added to the care plan and that it is regularly updated while it is possible to continue meeting the person's needs.

Workers need to be able to identify when the person is not happy and be skilled at gaining their trust so that they can talk about what is troubling them if they want to do so. They also need to be aware of occasions when service-users' emotional needs cannot be met by them and inform health and social work assessors.

In order to empower users, staff need to give to, or share power with, users in a variety of ways:

Settling in

It is often difficult to come into a new situation where friendships and ways of doing things are already established. Staff need to ensure that people's first visits are as welcoming and easy as possible for them. This can be done by:

- preparing other day service-users to welcome the new person;

- liaising with care-givers, whether formal or unpaid and with transport providers, so arrangements for getting ready for day care and coming back are clear to everyone involved;

- ensuring that the transport is suitable for their particular physical needs;

- ensuring that they know when their transport is going to arrive to pick them up.

What happens at the day service?

Staff can empower people by exchanging information with them, so that the users can contribute as much as is possible to the running of the day service. Staff can do this in a variety of ways, by:

- defining what it is they can offer now and in the future;

- working consistently towards offering individuals the chance to organise their own day as much as is possible;

- enabling users and carers to make suggestions as to how the service can develop through the use of white boards, question- naires, meetings and newsletters;

- encouraging service-users and carers to offer their own talents, however large or small;

- being persistent in offering opportunities for new developments, as users are known not to want to disturb the culture of the service that they find when they arrive. Some users will be well established in their routine and resist any innovations;

- enabling carers of people with dementia to share their knowledge of what the person particularly enjoyed doing in the past, so as to be able to offer opportunities to retain or regain those skills.

Does everyone have to do the same thing?

Staff need to use the space in the day service imaginatively in order to give as much choice of activity as possible, by:

- ensuring that there is somewhere for service-users to retreat to in order to read, rest and converse quietly;

- providing spaces for different activities;

- ensuring that they do not coerce people into doing activities;

- ensuring that people with similar interests can spend time together;

- ensuring that the needs of women and men are met. Assumptions can be made about activities only being suitable for men or women – they need to be offered to both. The needs of individual

79

men can readily be neglected as they tend to be the minority in day services;

- ensuring that any physical barriers to communication are dealt with, such as checking that people's hearing aids are working and sight needs are met;
- day centres also need to enable people to go shopping, go out on visits to places of interest, go for walks and so on.

What about food?

Meal times are one of the main parts of the day and are an opportunity for enjoyment as well as partly meeting people's nutritional needs. People living in the community do not necessarily eat very well and attendance at a day service can provide opportunities for observing and monitoring people's health and wellbeing.

Staff need to think about what food is offered and in what form? This will depend on:

- what other meals people eat in their day. For example, their main meal might be at the day centre or in the evening. Breakfast or a packed tea might be important for some people;
- their likes and dislikes;
- special dietary needs for medical reasons;
- whether they are vegetarian or vegan, eat fish or meat;
- religious and cultural preferences.

It is important for any food offered to be attractively presented to tempt people to eat. It may be important to provide nutritious snacks, including finger food at regular intervals through the day, so that people can eat when they are hungry.

Preparation of meals:

- people can help in large ways and small with the preparation of food, laying of tables and washing up. People can shell peas in a bowl on their laps, knead dough on a tray, butter bread, and so on;
- if there is a microwave oven and ready made snacks or potatoes, people can use it any time.

Flexibility in offering food means that people can choose what, when and where they want to eat. Attention needs to be paid to whether people's enjoyment of food will be spoilt by having to sit with others and be observed when their ability to eat is physically or mentally impaired. This may be dealt with by providing finger food. Strategies which do not disempower should be explored with them.

How can staff help individuals to be part of the group?

The way in which staff act with individuals whose behaviour means others may not want to be with them or who may be the subject of discrimination is crucial in showing everyone that those individuals are valued. Staff need to work with people to understand where their dislike or prejudice comes from, so that no one feels too rejected by the groups of people attending. It may be that despite all that staff do, individual's needs cannot be met within the day service environment and other ways of meeting their needs have to be found.

Links with volunteers, other day services providers and visitors.

Day services can enhance what they can offer by encouraging volunteers and visitors to contribute to the richness of their provision. They can:

- negotiate with other day services to share ideas and borrow equipment;

- brief outside visitors, including entertainers, therapists, reminiscence workers and teachers, about the needs of the service-users;

- encourage volunteers to be flexible. Some volunteers will be used to their routine and not want to change, particularly if they have ageist attitudes towards older disabled people – older than themselves, that is – the average age of volunteers in day centres is 70!

Does it continue to meet their needs?

- key workers and managers must be aware of when the person's needs change so much that they are no longer able to meet them;

- staff need to assist service-users and carers to be part of the overall review of the package of care which includes day services.

What happens to these links once people move into care?

- when people go into residential or nursing home care, they may want to continue to go to the day activities they were involved in for a while so as not to lose contact with their friends;

- workers may need to work to support these friendships, for example by ensuring that people have transport to visit each other if the service-user does not want to or is unable to continue to spend time in day centres, clubs and pubs.

Conclusion

Meeting individual needs within day services poses a challenge to those who staff them. Users of services need to be clear that their current and future needs can be met, that they are not just expected to fit into what exists but, on the contrary, are enabled to plan and run the services themselves as far as is possible.

Chapter Eleven

Enabling People to be Themselves in Residential Care

Disempowering Factors

A group of vulnerable people

In a home for older people, residents are perhaps not quite so dependent as those living in a nursing home or long-stay hospital, but the differences are merely of degree. In an age of scarce welfare resources, they would not be in a home at all if they did not need a considerable amount of assistance with their personal care or a high level of supervision because of mental frailty; this is particularly so since the changes heralded by the NHS and Community Care Act.

Anyone who lives all year round in the care of others is vulnerable. In addition, some will not have friends or family to advocate for them. Some will have family members whose anxiety is so relieved because their relative is 'safe' that they will not wish to hear that anything is wrong or cast a critical eye themselves over the establishment.

Who holds the power?

It must seem that the power lies anywhere but with the resident. The person may have had very little choice of home if their preferred one was not in the appropriate price bracket. Maybe the need for residential care was so immediate that it was not possible to wait for a vacancy in the preferred home, perhaps further increasing the vulnerability of the person by removing them from local ties and contacts and a familiar locality, or making it more difficult for family and friends to visit. In a survey (Hobman et al 1994):

"nearly half of that sample (100) had experienced the decision to come into a home as one which was taken by someone else"

In any case, it is with the owner, be it the social services department or a commercial business, that the power lies. The owner and their on-the-spot manager will resource and furnish the home, staff it, pay for the food. It is they who gatekeep, liaise with other professionals, even have a chat with the family in the office. A resident can feel insecure and powerless in this situation.

Institutionalisation

The word 'institutionalisation' describes a process which appears to affect all establishments (institutions) – the inevitable tendency of staff to treat people who live together not as individuals but as a group. In this process, individuality causes difficulty and is slowly but surely, though not consciously, eradicated.

It is a 'problem' because it requires the staff to listen to each person and respond differently to each individual. This requires time, energy and commitment. It is much easier to treat everyone as a group with the same needs and desires.

For example, if on a unit of seven residents everyone has a nap after lunch, then staff can have their own break or get on with household tasks within the home, do their record-writing or any other of the myriad tasks which need doing. However, if only a couple want to nap, one would like a member of staff to read the paper to her, another needs help writing a letter, a third wants to sit and chat and the fourth wants someone to help him over the road to the shops, then the demands on staff become much higher. It is much more challenging to respond to individual need and, therefore, easier to pretend such needs don't exist by not doing anything to invite their expression and gently to maintain the suggestion that people are 'very happy' to nap after lunch.

Another example of institutionalisation is that we expect people to adapt to situations which, outside of the institution, we would be horrified by. For instance, we expect people to be happy to share a bedroom. It is regrettable that although standards have risen sufficiently in residential care to outlaw three and four-bedded rooms, double rooms remain. They are sometimes all that are available in the private sector to those unable to finance themselves. We expect people who up to this point have run their own households and never shared a bedroom with any but their partner, if anybody, to share with a total stranger. Either person in this enforced sharing may be embarrassed by the lack of privacy for their personal care needs, may have completely different sleep patterns, may be mentally unable to form much of a relationship and so on. The fact that people do come to 'happily' share a room with someone unknown is merely a sign of the strength of the disempowerment caused by institution-alisation.

Any new resident can rapidly become groomed (or conditioned) to accept the loss of their individuality and forget their rights in this respect. 'Fitting' is important where people are encouraged to spend most of the day in the lounge and in the company of others. The pressure can be considerable on a new resident or on one who is not particularly interested in 'fitting in'. People who are seen to be 'different', perhaps because they are gay, come from a black or minority ethnic group or have dementia, may particularly fear that their feelings and needs are not going to be recognised or met. New residents will soon see the need to 'fit' if they are to settle quickly and anyway may be too vulnerable and grief-stricken at the turn their life has taken to expect anything else.

To empower people in these circumstances is very challenging for staff. It does not happen automatically but needs awareness and commitment. What follows are a few ideas to help.

Empowerment Strategies

Information

Like everyone else in receipt of services from powerful organisations, people in residential care need information. It is often assumed that they don't, that it was enough that they were told about the facilities in the home and the neighbourhood when they first came to live there, how much they could bring with them to furnish their room, when visitors could come and so on.

However, when events occur which are not within one's own control to organise, as necessarily happens in a residential home, then people feel that lack of control much more if they do not have information. One of the challenges for residential care staff is to present that information in a way which is meaningful to each individual and can be retained by them. Some may need to be told, some may need to be told repeatedly, other may prefer information to be written down. Occasionally, a person may need a tape made so they can listen to it when they need to.

Some strategies for handing power over to residents through information might be:

- *What is happening today?* Calenders and diaries can be encouraged in two specific ways. *Firstly,* there can be a calender for the home, or unit within the home. This could include planned events, i.e. church services, outings, entertainments, etc. This will enable residents to be more involved, to anticipate, will provide a talking point and of course give them time and opportunity to decide if they want be there. Such a calender can also record the manager and staff on duty. *Secondly,* individuals can be encouraged to keep a personal diary or calender. Most people in their own homes have somewhere to record a future visit by family member, birthdays, a hospital or hairdresser's appointment. This should be continued in the home. The effect of such information is to help people preserve the sense of days being different from each other, enable them to plan and choose by anticipation and feel some control over the comings and goings in their lives.

- **What's for lunch?** Within this generation of older people, many men have never been much involved in the planning and preparation of food. However, most women will have spent time every day thinking about food – what to have, how to make it, how to vary it and so on. Relieved as many will be not to have to worry about meals any more, it will nevertheless leave a gap in their lives for the whole ritual to be totally removed from them. In information terms, many residents will feel less powerless if they know what is on the menu, what the choices are and even the opportunity to hear from the cook how different dishes are made. Such information should be written – on printed menus or on wipe-boards – so that short-term memory loss will not pose a problem.

- **Who's working today?** Good managers in residential homes will try to ensure that groups of residents have the same staff as much as possible and are not subject to an endless stream of different care assistants. Nevertheless, it is inevitable that over the course of a week or a month, residents will receive their personal care from a number of staff. Clear name tags will avoid the embarrassment of being helped in the toilet by someone, however familiar, whose name has been forgotten. Residents will feel more able to call for help if they know the names of the people on duty and, where residents are more able to differentiate between staff by use of their names, relationships will be aided.

Time

In terms of staff, residential homes are run very tightly. Competition is fierce and money in short supply. Numbers of care assistants are pared to the minimum. When there are so many care and household tasks to be seen to, time to sit and talk to a resident, to enable them to follow some activity or to keep in touch with a friend or relative seems impossible to find.

Apart from the general feelings of powerlessness this causes, to the extent that residents may feel guilty in asking for some assistance and will agree that acts of virtual neglect are acceptable because the staff are 'so busy',comes a loss of the very skills residents need to hang on to if they are to survive in this environment. It is a lot easier to 'do for' than 'do with' when time is at a premium. For example, a care assistant will find it much quicker to cut up all of the food on the plate into small pieces than provide some simple eating aids. Such incidents seem small in themselves and appear to save valuable time but an amalgamation will lead to a serious reduction in the resident's skills and to greater dependency.

To counter this, staff can use some positive strategies:

- *Be there for the person!* Although time may be of the essence, it is important that during that time when the staff member is with the resident, however short, he or she is focused on the person and their individual needs. If the resident feels that the care assistant is very rushed, they will agree to short cuts, to 'being seen to', and will experience a loss of power. If the care assistant takes the attitude, even when time is short, that needs must be met in a way that maintains independence and dignity, then residents will feel more empowered in spite of considerable physical dependency.

- *Let the person know how much time is available.* Residents will often appear to 'waste' the brief time available to them by chatting, not being ready, asking for help with inessentials. Often this is a desire to keep the care assistant there longer. However, if staff share openly with the resident how much time is available, then they can agree together on what needs to be done. Perhaps time can be agreed later, at a less busy time, to spend on other aspects.

- *Rethink priorities.* Care assistants will have many tasks to achieve in the course of the day and perhaps spending time with residents on undefined tasks may come very low on that list. Indeed, in some homes it may not appear at all. There will be many days, however, when activity will not be so high, when perhaps a corner can be cut on bed-making or other tasks, to free up the ten or fifteen minutes to spend with a resident in a way which will empower them by treating them as more than a task to be seen to. Managers can assist in this by ensuring that staff work to a 24-hour cycle, so that 'household' tasks are fitted around the individual needs of the residents throughout the day and night.

Seeing the whole person – use of interpersonal skills

All the time in the world, however, will be inadequate to empower people if staff attitudes are not positive. It can be painful and difficult to work with this group of people. They remind us continuously of our own mortality and that of parents and friends whom we love. Incipient dementia can be confusing for staff, hearing problems irritating, lack of mobility frustrating and these conditions sometimes appear so much to the fore that the personality behind gets lost. For the person themselves, of course, such focus on weakness and disability further makes them feel small, worthless, a nuisance, with little right to power or control in their lives.

Various strategies can help staff to come to know and have regard for the whole person:

- *Listen to the resident, learn about them and their past.* A task-orientated approach, often adopted less as a policy and more as a way of getting everything done, leaves staff little opportunity to get to know the person, their background, thoughts and wishes and indeed offers a shield against the pain of such encounters. However, giving people the encouragement to talk and showing interest in their unique experience will assist them in feeling valued, not dumped, discarded and finished. Where people have a degree of dementia, life story work as described in Chapter 8 can enable past experiences to be captured and to be a point of reference for both resident and care assistant.

- *Record interests, emotional needs and aspirations on the care plan.* Care plans can seem to relate to physical care only. However, if residents are encouraged to record there what they still wish to achieve and care assistants work out with them how to go about this (in much the same way as they work out how best to assist in bathing, for example), then the resident will come to see the home as a place where not only their physical needs are met, but where they still have a chance of living some kind of enjoyable or meaningful life.

- *Resist ageist attitudes.* These are the sorts of ways of thinking that conclude that older people, particularly with the level of frailty seen in residential homes, are 'past it', no longer have individual hopes and preferences, don't deserve opportunities and are basically waiting to die in comfort. If staff can discard these values, they will inevitably find themselves supporting and encouraging residents to express themselves and find worthwhile outlets and take pleasure in their achievements. This will include encouraging relationships, both friendships and sexual contacts, acknowledging conflict – in short, the whole range that we all experience in our contacts with other people – whilst also ensuring the most vulnerable are neither abused nor exploited.

Choices

What choices are really available to people in residential care? Perhaps they did not even really choose to be there, but gave in to the various pressures, subtle and not so subtle, placed on them as they became less able to manage at home.

Within the routines of the home, managers may pride themselves on being able to offer residents breakfast in their bedroom or the dining-room, or two choices of main dish at lunch-time. Perhaps barriers between day and night-care staff have been broken down so people can go to bed earlier or later as they wish. These choices, whilst limited, are not to be dismissed lightly as they have often been carved painfully out of institutional life; often, like much else, by stretching scarce staff resources.

Yet much more could be done:

- *Individual choice in food.* The centralised kitchen, whilst efficient in many ways, also militates against individual choice. For cost-effectiveness, there may be very little option to this method of meal preparation for the main meal of the day and the cook and responsible manager will need to ensure, by continuous discussion with residents, that the menu and limited choices do really reflect the food that people like to eat. Frozen meals and microwaves can, however, do much to stretch the choices on offer. Care must also be taken that people who prefer other foods for medical, cultural, religious or other reasons, also have a real choice. 'The vegetarian option' is after all not going to provide any choice at all to the strict vegetarian.

89

However, at other mealtimes, it should be possible for people to have what they actually want, within the range of foods appropriate to that meal. It is not easy to change from mass catering to many individually-prepared dishes, but persistence and good organisation can make this happen. The pay-off for residents is active participation in the events of the day, choice and greater control over one important area of their lives.

- *Encourage residents to utilise the different parts of the home.* Too often the pattern of the day is that once people have had their breakfast they will settle in their lounge for the rest of the day, making brief excursions only to go to the toilet or to the dining-room. The result is a lack of bustle or activity or purposefulness, leading to the inevitable all-day napping in the armchair.

Room ownership is challenging to staff who may be used to wandering in and out of people's rooms several times a day without informing the resident. But, if people are really encouraged to regard their room as their own and staff respect this as much as if they actually rented or owned the room then residents would be happier to spend time in there with their own things, TV, visitors, etc. If their rooms are not remorselessly cleansed and tidied by domestic staff, they may do their own pottering about, dusting and tidying in itself being a good form of exercise for frail people. They will then choose to spend time in the lounge when wishing to socialise, or to give a hand in the dining-room or garden, or visit old and new acquaintances in the lounges of other day centres.

- *What would you like to do today?* Staff can encourage residents to think about and take responsibility for their day, any tasks or activities they want to get on with, any events planned or unplanned. This will prevent the 'every day feels the same' syndrome and enable staff to use their time to suit the resident's needs and choices.

Sharing power

In the introduction to this chapter, mention was made of how the power relationship between the owner/manager/staff and resident is weighted away from the older person. All the strategies discussed in this chapter so far will do something towards redressing that balance by empowering people to feel more in control of their lives, more able to express their individuality and, in addition, will have staff on hand who really want this to happen.

There are some other actions which will assist this process in a slightly different way.

- *Encourage the power of the group.* Residents could be enabled to form a group to discuss home life and ask for changes. This needs to be far away from the old residents' committee idea which favoured the stronger individual but totally disempowered the confused, timid and hard-of-hearing. Various methods may have to be tried, but perhaps small groups of residents with their regular staff who are committed to listening and acting on ideas suggested may be a useful starting-point. In other circumstances, it can be useful to bring in an independent person to enable a group of residents to state their views.

- *The role of the keyworker.* Keyworkers in residential care can become important in a resident's life. They are often responsible for assisting with bathing, birthday celebrations, shopping and so on. Often a special relationship will be formed and the keyworker may be the first or only one to perceive causes of unhappiness or unmet needs and aspirations. It is important that residents are allowed to choose their keyworkers as much as possible and that the role is supported by managers so that keyworkers are enabled to become important advocates for residents, promoting their wishes and raising the profile of their needs.

- *Involve residents in planning.* Many people in residential care would not wish to be involved in planning services in any formal way; some would be mentally or physically unable to cope with any planning meeting or forum. However, there are people in residential care who lived busy, active lives, professionally or voluntarily, involved in many different kinds of organisations and have many useful skills, knowledge and experience. Such people may have much to contribute in a well-led planning forum with appropriate support and would feel appreciated and valued for what they still have to offer.

Checking it out/making it easy to complain

Most people find it difficult to complain. This is particularly true of vulnerable people, but is not surprising when we consider the state of disempowerment of residents in homes. People have to feel they deserve better before they think it is worth complaining, that someone will listen to them and value them enough to help change things. In addition, residents may be afraid to complain. To complain may invite retribution and make things worse rather than better; residents may fear what may happen if they make a complaint against a person from whom they receive personal care. These worries must be put to rest for people to feel able to complain.

- *Making it easy to complain.* Feed-back about life in the home, good and bad, can be actively encouraged by staff and managers so that comments and criticisms are received in a positive light. If staff have a very open attitude about learning how to improve service, people will not feel so frightened to comment. Residents need to know who to speak to or write to. People with dementia may need an advocate to observe and comment on their behalf.

- *Complaints need to be acted on speedily.* People will be empowered to complain if they can see that their comments are being acted upon or they get feed-back about any complaint they make,

- *Find other ways of discovering what residents think.* How often do staff and managers really ask what residents think of the service they spend all their working lives providing? Various ways can be used, occasionally involving more objective and arms-length methods – for example, an independent inspection, a consultation process by a voluntary agency and questionnaires.

Conclusion

There are particular challenges for staff in residential homes if they wish to empower people. There is the natural tendency of any large establishment to be run for its staff rather than its residents, with many unwritten rules governing behaviour, or for residents to be regarded as a group rather than individuals. A highly individualised model of care can empower residents. Considering all the strategies in detail will make this a reality for people living in homes.

References

1. Age Concern (1995) "Home Comforts", Chapter 9

2. Bhalla, A. and Blakemore, K. (1981) "Elders of the Ethnic Minority Groups", All Faiths For One Race, Birmingham

3. Brearley, P. (1975) "Social Work Ageing and Society", Routledge and Kegan Paul

4. Dearden, C. and Becker, S. (1995) "Young Carers, The Facts", Community Care

5. Department of Health, Social Services Inspectorate: "Care Management and Assessment – A Practitioner's Guide"

6. Fennell, G. et al, (1981) "Day Centres for the Elderly in East Anglia", Centre for East Anglia Studies

7. Fennell, G. et al, (1983) "Elderly People in the Community: Their Service Needs", HMSO

8. Griffiths, (1989) "Caring for People – Community Care in the Next Decade and Beyond", White Paper, HMSO

9. Hobman, D., Hollingbury, R., Smith, J., Means, R. and Lart, R. (1994) "More Power to Our Elders", Counsel and Care

10. Howe, D. (198) "An Introduction to Social Work Theory", Vol: 4, Ashgate Publishing Ltd

11. Howe, D. (1987) Vol: 6 op cit

12. Levin, E. et al (1989) "Families, Services and Confusion in Old Age", Gower, Aldershot

13. Nissel, M. and Bonnerjea, L. (1982) "Family Care of the Handicapped Elderly. Who Pays?" Policy Studies Institute, London

14. Norman, A. J. (1980) "Rights and Risks: a Discussion Document on Civil Liberty in Old London", NCCOP, Vol: 39

15. Parker, R. (1990) "Kaleidoscope of Care", NISW

16. Phillipson, C. (1982) "Capitalism and the Construction of Old Age", Vol: 96, Macmillan Press

17. Sainsbury, E. (1975) "Social Work with Families", Vol: 1, Routledge and Kegan Paul

18. Smale, G. (1993) "Empowerment, assessment, care management and the skilled worker", NISW

19. Stevenson, O. and Parsloe, P. (1993) "Community Care and Empowerment", Joseph Rowntree Foundation

20. Social Services Inspectorate, (1995) "Moving On – Report of Arrangements for the Discharge of Older People from Hospital", HMSO

21. Taylor, M., Hoyes, L., Lart, R. and Means, R. (1992) "User Empowerment in Community Care", Vol: 3, SAUS Publications

22. Tester, S. (1989) "Caring by Day: a study of day care services for older people", Centre for Policy on Ageing

Bibliography

Beresford, P. (1993) "A Challenge to Change", NISW

Bornat, J., Pereira, C., Pilgrim, D. and Williams, F. (1993) "Community Care", a reader, Open University

DoH, SSI (1992) "Care Management and Assessment: Carers' Guide", HMSO

Griffiths, Sir Roy (1989) "Caring for People, Community Care in the Next Decade Beyond", HMSO

Hobman, D., Hollingbury, R., Smith, J., Means, R. and Lart, R. (1994) "More Power to Our Elders", Counsel and Care

Sinclair, I., Parker, R., Leat, D. and Williams, J. (1990) "The Kaleidoscope of Care", NISW, HMSO

Smale, G. (1993) "Empowerment, Assessment, Care Management and the Skilled Worker", NISW

Stevenson, O. and Parsloe, P. (1993) "Community Care and Empowerment", Joseph Rowntree Foundation

Taylor, M., Hoyes, L., Lart, R. and Means, R. (1992) "User Empowerment in Community Care. Unravelling Issues", SAUS Publication

Index